THE HOUSE OF BUSTA

INTRODUCTION

THE HOUSE OF BUSTA
ITS TRIUMPHS AND TRAGEDIES

D. HILDA PETERSON

The Shetland Times Ltd.,
Lerwick.
2000
The House of Busta

The House of Busta
Its triumphs and tragedies

ISBN 1 898852 59 6

First published by The Shetland Times Ltd., 2000.

Reprinted 2001

Cover illustration by Alexa Rutherford.

British Library Cataloguing-in-Publication Data
A catalogue record for this book is available from the British Library

Printed and published by
The Shetland Times Ltd.,
Prince Alfred Street,
Lerwick, Shetland ZE1 0EP, UK.

I dedicate this book to my husband and family.

CONTENTS

FOREWORD

While most people in Shetland have heard of the Busta story, few know more than the basic facts - the tragic accident when four brothers, including the heir to the Busta estate, were drowned; the action of Barbara Pitcairn in retrieving from John's clothing, after his body had been recovered, the document which proved that they had been secretly married; and the long legal battle which saddled the estate with debt.

In this book Hilda Peterson has clothed the bare bones of the story, taking us behind the scenes as she describes in detail life in the mansion and the croft house, the work that went on in the fields and on the beaches, where the vitally important fish were salted, dried and prepared for export to the Continent.

Throughout the narrative runs the tragic story of Barbara Pitcairn, who was despised by Lady Busta yet triumphed in the end when her son Gideon inherited the estate. It is said that her ghost still roams the house looking for her son.

This book is well researched and well written, giving an insight into life in Shetland in the mid 18th century as well as being a valuable addition to the islands' literature.

James R. Nicolson

ACKNOWLEDGEMENTS

I must first of all thank James R. Nicolson, Scalloway for taking time to review this book, for his helpful advice and for kindly writing the Foreword.

I am indebted to Mrs Agnes Davidson, Falkirk for her expertise in typing the manuscript, also Mrs Kathleen Simpson, Lerwick.

Finally, my thanks to Derek Bingham for his initial encouragement to proceed with this project.

Chapter 1

WELCOME TO BUSTA HOUSE

"Welcome to Busta House," said Thomas Gifford as he carried his young wife over the threshold and set her gently down in the large hallway.

"Thank you," whispered Elizabeth, "it is lovely, I will go to my room, I wish to change after the long journey."

A young girl appeared, "Beth," said Thomas, "this is Lady Busta, please show her to her room."

"Yes Sir. Madam?"

As Elizabeth went upstairs Thomas gave a sigh. He had done so much to make the house modern and attractive for the home-coming. He was a kind, sensitive person and a little upset by his wife's reaction. He shrugged his shoulders and supposed he would get used to Elizabeth's moods in time.

As Beth opened the bedroom door, Elizabeth caught her breath. She had never seen such a beautiful room before. A four-poster bed stood at the opposite side of the room with drapings of a heavy cream, covered in small sprays of flowers and edged with a deep frill. There were curtains at the window to match. Shetland handmade rugs covered the floor of dark, polished wood. Behind the door was a large wardrobe, there was a chest-of-drawers, washstand and a dressing-table near the window.

"Thank you Beth," said Elizabeth as the maid withdrew, "I shall be glad if you will bring me some hot water."

As Elizabeth drew off her gloves she felt ashamed at the curt reply she had given her husband, but everything was so new to her, he would understand.

When Beth had left the room Elizabeth sat down on one of the little bedroom chairs.

It had been quite a day! She had wakened early to a lovely, sunny morning in Scalloway. From her bedroom window at her home, 'West shore,' she looked out across the calm waters of the sea to the island of Trondra. The old

Scalloway Castle looked gaunt and eerie against the hill of Easterhoull in the background.

She would miss the lovely view, but Thomas had assured her that the view from Busta House was even more beautiful.

The wedding had been wonderful, her parents providing a lavish meal for their guests. She would miss her parents and the walled garden where she and her mother worked among the trees and flowers.

Elizabeth and her mother were good companions. Mrs. Mitchell had taught her daughter well in the art of managing a large house, so Elizabeth was quite prepared to tackle the awesome role as Mistress of Busta House.

Beth knocked on the door and entered with a ewer of hot water. Just as she was retiring Elizabeth asked her to undo the buttons on her leather gaiters. They were stiff being so new.

Travelling from Scalloway to Brae by open boat had been quite enjoyable as it was a calm day. The boat also carried many beautiful presents the couple had received.

......

Thomas rang a bell in the hall.

"Yes sir?" queried Beth.

"I wish afternoon tea served in the sitting-room upstairs in half an hour. You can tell Lady Busta when it is ready."

"Sir," Beth curtsied and left the room.

After a wash and change of clothing, Elizabeth began to feel hungry. A knock came to the door.

"Come in," she called.

"May I show Madam to the sitting-room? Mr. Gifford has ordered tea to be served." Beth explained.

"Have you been here long?" Elizabeth asked, "and do you like working at Busta House?"

"Two years, Ma'am. Yes, I like working for Mr. Gifford. He is very kind to us," replied Beth. She ushered Lady Busta into the sitting-room and Thomas jumped up from his chair as she entered.

"Come and have a cup of tea to refresh you, you must be quite tired," he said.

"There is one thing I must say first," Elizabeth interrupted.

Thomas looked worried – what could be wrong? Surely he had thought of everything for his wife's comfort.

"I want to thank you for this beautiful home, and to say I think it is magnificent," she said in one breath.

2

Thomas could hardly believe his ears. His wife was a woman of few words, she certainly must have been impressed by his efforts, to make such a speech of thanks!

"Nothing but the best will do for you," he smiled.

Taking her arm, he led her to a chair near the fire. They enjoyed the tea and scones then sat and chatted.

"I do trust you will like it here, my dear," Thomas said, "I shall be away on business most days but will look forward to returning in the evenings for dinner with you. It has been so lonely on my own here. Come, I will show you the family portraits in this room."

"Tell me," said Elizabeth as Thomas got to the last portrait, "when did the Giffords first come to Busta?"

"That is a long story, my dear," sighed Thomas, relieved to think his wife was at all interested. "Sit down and I shall tell you."

"In the year 1570, King James VI made his half-brother, Robert Stewart, Earl of Orkney and Lord of Zetland. Earl Robert not only took possession of the Earldom of Orkney and Lordship of Zetland but the bishop rents also. He became sole proprietor of the crown rents. He was a selfish, greedy man. All affairs sacred or evil were ordered for his good and pleasure.

When he arrived in Shetland he built a house at Sumburgh, called 'West-house', also one at Delting, called 'Wethersta'. The latter he sold to my great, great, great grandfather, Andrew Gifford in 1583, and it has been in the Gifford family ever since. Earl Robert's son Patrick built the Scalloway Castle."

"I know that Thomas," Elizabeth sighed. "I have often visited it, but never Wethersta. I had no idea that it was owned by the Stewarts also."

"Apparently," continued Thomas, "Robert Stewart reserved two or three rooms at Wethersta for his own use. I have heard say that Grandfather was anything but pleased when he heard the Earl would be visiting Wethersta. He was a cruel, hard man as was his son Patrick after him."

Thomas took a deep breath,

"Did you know that James Hepburn – Earl of Bothwell – was created Duke of Orkney by Mary, Queen of Scotland, so that he would be a man with a title, because she was determined to marry him? It is said he had a hand in the murder of the Queen's former husband, Henry, Lord Darnley, and when suspected went to stay in Orkney. He was not a good man," Thomas finished.

"When did the Queen marry this James Hepburn?" queried Elizabeth.

"It was on the 15th May, 1567," replied her husband, "that the marriage took place in the palace of Holyrood House, by Adam Bothwell who was Bishop of Orkney. When James was not accepted in Orkney or Zetland, he went on to Norway where he was taken prisoner. He was sent to Copenhagen and put in prison there, where he spent ten years until he died.

3

"When Robert Stewart was created Earl of Orkney and Lord of Zetland, he was prior of Holyrood House, which title he exchanged with Adam Bothwell for his bishopric in Orkney. Am I boring you with all this history, my dear?"

"On the contrary, I am fascinated by it. Having only heard snippets of it now and then it is interesting to hear the full story. So what happened to Patrick in the end?" she asked.

"He became so vicious in his rules and regulations that the inhabitants complained frequently to the King who took possession of the islands into his own hands. He appointed Sir James Stewart, Lord Ochiltree, to take over as His Majesty's chamberlain and imprisoned Patrick Stewart. In 1614, Earl Patrick was taken from prison in Glasgow to Edinburgh where he was tried for crimes of treason and oppression. He was found guilty and beheaded that same year in February.

"Our family is descended from John Gifford of Sheriffhall. In 1574 his second son John was made a minister in the parish of Northmavine. It was his son Andrew who bought the old mansion house of Wethersta from Earl Robert and at the same time acquired the lands of Busta.

"Andrew's son John married Marjory Bruce. They had an unusually large family – ten sons and fourteen daughters! It was their son Robert who was first in Busta. My father John Gifford, died in 1705 and I was sole heir to this estate," Thomas smiled.

"Beth will have unpacked my tapestry by now, I would like her to bring it to me," said Elizabeth as she rang the bell beside the fireplace.

It was not long before Beth appeared, and as she cleared the teacups away, Elizabeth asked her to bring her sewing.

"When you come back, Beth, you might put some more peats in the basket and light the lamps," Thomas told her.

"Yes sir." she replied.

......

Thomas Gifford was indeed a busy man. Apart from his estate and his business in the foreign fishing markets, he also held the official capacity of Steward-Depute, holding courts when necessary throughout the country districts.

Elizabeth was occupied in the mornings in connection with the house duties for the day, interviewing Martha, the housekeeper, also the cook concerning menus for lunch and dinner.

If the weather was fine, Elizabeth would take her little black poodle, Pierre for a walk over the hills or down to the beach. After returning she would relax in the chair at the sitting-room window and await her husband's return from work.

4

......

The gig came down the road on the green headland, passed the dove-cot, the sign of a wealthy family, descended a steep hill, passed the little harbour, skirted the high garden wall and approached the massive front door through tall, wrought-iron gates.

Alighting, Thomas Gifford's eyes strayed to the Coat of Arms placed above the lintel. He was very proud of it. Connected to the house of Tweeddale, the family escutcheon wore the Tweeddale arms along with their own.

Entering through the front door, Thomas handed his coat and stick to Beth, then climbed the wide, carpeted, stone staircase to the sitting-room, and after greeting his wife asked how she had spent her day.

As the gong sounded for dinner, Thomas accompanied Elizabeth downstairs to the dining-room where an elaborate meal awaited them.

The dining-room was lit by candles held in bracket-sconces on the walls and candles on the table. The lights threw a cosy glow over the dark furniture and curtains. Oak beams stood out against the lighter ceiling.

Thomas was dressed elegantly for dinner and looked very smart.

Elizabeth wore a peach satin frock which did justice to her lovely figure. She also wore a pearl necklace and long pearl earrings to match, and her hair was done in the latest fashion. (She was amazed to find Beth had a flair for hair-dressing and very thankful too.)

Coffee was served in the drawing-room, where a cheerful fire burned. It was the best time of day.

That evening Thomas told his wife he had to go to London for a few days on business.

"I hope you will not mind being on your own dear, I do not like having to leave you," he said.

"I will be fine," Elizabeth assured him, "there is so much to see about, I hardly have a spare minute. Going over the household duties with Martha and giving Bertha and cook their orders for the day. Would you mind if I asked the gardener about new plants for the garden? I would like a Hawthorn hedge at the top of the steps in the back garden. It would help to keep the wind off the flowers below."

"Yes, that would be excellent," agreed Thomas. "I am sure whatever you choose will be appropriate. Is there anything you would like me to bring back from London for you?"

"I have everything I need, thank you," she replied. "Oh, please pass my scissors from that little table. I keep losing things. It was my thimble yesterday".

A smile passed across Thomas' face, he now had an idea for a present to bring home for his wife, he was sure she would find useful.

5

After breakfast the next day, Thomas asked James to put his portmanteau into the gig ready for the journey.

Turning to Elizabeth he kissed her goodbye. As she stood framed in the doorway, with her pale blue frock and hair falling round her shoulders, Thomas thought he had never seen her looking so beautiful. Quite a picture. As the gig turned down the drive on its journey, he returned her wave.

Elizabeth went to her room. She had been so brave about staying at the house on her own, but now she broke down and wept. After a moment she dried her eyes, it would never do for Beth to find her looking like this! She put a little cologne on a handkerchief and dabbed her face. Feeling more sure of herself she went to the sitting-room to prepare for the daily interviews.

Meanwhile Thomas travelled to Brae in the gig to hire a boat to take him to Olnafirth, paying six shillings for his fare, James could not row his employer to Voe this trip as he had duties to see to at Busta House.

Arriving at Voe Thomas alighted from the boat and hired a pony to take him to Catfirth, to catch a ferry-boat to Lerwick.

His cost was seven shillings for the pony, and a few pence for the boy.

Several people were travelling to Lerwick that day so they were rowed in a six-oared boat, their fare being one pound.

In Lerwick harbour the sixern drew alongside a large sailing boat, which was bound for Leith, and discharged any passengers wishing to travel on her.

An hour after leaving the harbour, a gong sounded on board the ship announcing a meal. Thomas went down to the cabin and was given a seat beside the captain, at the table.

"Good evening Gifford," the captain greeted him, "it is nice to have your company tonight. How are things with you? Foreign trade going well?"

"Excellent! Trade is booming right now, it couldn't be better," answered Thomas proudly. "The boats come mostly from Bremen, Denmark, Sweden and lately Norway, Spain and Portugal."

After a pleasant meal the captain queried, "Would you like to see Mousa from the deck?"

"I would, it is a lovely night," replied Thomas.

The sea was becoming quite choppy as he descended the steps to the cabin again. Round the walls were two-tier berths. Lying in his bunk Thomas was soon asleep. The ship tossed and rolled but on the whole it was a good journey.

When the ship arrived at Leith, gigs were waiting to take passengers to their destinations, while others stayed on board to travel to London.

Thomas disembarked with the first lot of passengers and entering a gig, told the driver to take him to Edinburgh. After one or two days of business there, he boarded a coach for London. Travelling the hot, dusty streets, Thomas' thoughts often reverted to the picture of Elizabeth framed in the doorway, waving him farewell. He felt he would do anything for a breath of fresh Shetland air!

Thomas had a number of offices to visit in connection with business. He did not have much spare time, but he was determined to have time to buy Elizabeth's present. He climbed the stairs of a large department store, to the furniture floor, and asked the assistant if he had any ladies sewing boxes in mahogany?

"Yes, sir, come this way," he said. "There are different styles. Some sit on a stool or table but this latest model is self-standing. It is divided into sections inside. A lovely piece of furniture, you'll agree?"

"I will take that one," said Thomas, and after paying asked for the box to be delivered to his hotel that day. He could imagine Elizabeth's delight when she saw it!

The journey home by boat from London was uneventful, but not fast enough for Thomas. He was longing to see his wife again.

Elizabeth too had missed her husband and had a lovely meal awaiting his return.

"It was good to see James at Olnafirth to pick me up," Thomas told her. "There are several packages I bought in London, the pony-carrier is taking them from Catfirth to Voe so James will bring them in soon. One of them contains the present I promised you," he said proudly. "I did not forget you, in fact, I thought a lot about you and wished I could have come home sooner. It was so hot in London, I shall never grumble about the cold weather here again!"

In the drawing room after dinner that evening Thomas rang the bell.

"Beth, please ask James to bring the box here marked for Lady Busta."

"Yes, sir," answered Beth going off to find James.

Setting the box on the floor, James asked, "Shall I open it for you sir?"

"Yes, just remove the outer wrapping," Thomas told him.

Once James had left the room, Elizabeth went over to the box and started to tear off the paper excitedly.

"Thomas, what is it?" she queried when she found a wooden box on legs. "I have never seen anything like this before. What is it for?"

"Open it up and you will see," said Thomas smiling.

"Oh! a sewing-box," exclaimed Elizabeth, "I can have it right beside me as I do my tapestry. How wonderful. I shall not misplace my scissors or thimble now. Thank you so much." And so saying she put her arms around Thomas' neck and kissed him.

Thomas was delighted that his present had brought such a rewarding response!

7

The sewing-box was the topic of conversation when anyone came to call. The couple were fond of entertaining and many a fine meal was enjoyed at Busta House. Cook excelled herself by making the most delicious dishes. The wines too were varied and rare often being presents given to Thomas Gifford from his clients.

Lady Busta enjoyed entertaining her friends to afternoon tea. The tea was supplied in especially made wood boxes lined with foil, and usually containing several different varieties. Sugar too was a scarce commodity and Elizabeth was proud to put it on the tea-table.

This evening, after the box had been opened, the couple sat and chatted over the events of the past weeks. Thomas loved his pipe and would sit and carefully fill the bowl with his favourite tobacco, light it, and lie back in his easy chair with his feet on a stool, watching his wife sewing.

Chapter 2

VISIT TO WETHERSTA

"I shall have to get a pony for you," said Thomas, "I would like to go riding together. There are many beautiful places of interest around here, but they are difficult to walk to. I am glad I brought Jasper up. He is larger than the Shetland ponies; I need the extra height for my legs! I shall look out for a smaller horse for you though. It would be nice to ride to Wethersta, across the water, where my cousin lives."

Not long after this conversation Thomas had business to see to again in Leith. While there, visiting a friend, who had a large estate, his friend said, "What about a ride today Thomas?"

"That would suit me fine," was the reply.

Entering the stables Thomas was amazed at the beautiful beasts his friend owned. Having bought Jasper from him, Thomas now asked if he had a suitable pony for Elizabeth. His friend selected a quiet, peaceable little mare, a bit larger than a Shetland pony, and said he would ship it north. Thomas was highly delighted.

On reaching home, Thomas said to Elizabeth that he had not brought anything for her on this trip – she pretended to be upset!

"Well," said Thomas, "it was a bit on the big side for my pocket!" He laughed, "You'll see it all in good time."

Two weeks went by, then three and Elizabeth was quite anxious incase her husband had forgotten about her present. It had been very stormy weather.

One morning after breakfast James knocked on the door.

"Excuse me sir, but your surprise for Lady Busta has arrived," he said disappearing out of the door.

"Come my love," said Thomas putting a hand under her elbow, "I do trust you will like her."

"Her?" repeated Elizabeth, "whatever can it be? I have little Pierre and you have your big dogs. Whatever–" she began as James opened the front door.

And there stood the most beautiful pony Elizabeth had ever set eyes on.

"Thomas, she is wonderful," she began, going over slowly to the mare, "I shall call her Pride. She needs something to eat right away. I shall get changed and come to the stable. James and I will see that she is washed down, brushed and given a feed."

Thomas led Elizabeth reluctantly back into the house.

"What do you think of her?" he asked.

"She is the best present I have ever had," she answered. "Now we shall be able to go and visit Wethersta instead of going by boat!"

At breakfast next day Thomas tapped the weather-glass.

"The glass is quite steady at the moment," he commented to his wife, "I think it should keep reasonably fine for a ride to see Andrew this afternoon. What do you say dear?"

"I would love to go today," Elizabeth answered eagerly, "I shall be able to wear the new riding gloves you gave me. The house does not look far from here, just across the voe. How long is it by road?"

"I think about three miles or so," was the reply. "The road is good as far as Brae but beyond that it is a moor track. I propose to extend the road as far as Wethersta in the near future. What a blessing the road from here to Brae has been. I have been enabled to employ many men to do the work."

After lunch, Elizabeth went to her room to dress for the ride. Beth had laid out the appropriate clothes on the bed with hat, gloves and a scarf.

Elizabeth had loved riding at home in Scalloway and one day she and her brother rode into Lerwick. A four-mile stretch of road ran from the Tingwall valley into the town on the south side.

Donning her riding habit of long green skirt, jacket and leather boots, Elizabeth made her way downstairs to the back door where James had Jasper and Pride ready for mounting.

The waves were gently lapping the shore as they passed the Booth on their way to climb the hill leading to Brae.

"Aren't the white pigeons beautiful sitting on the dove-cot. They make quite a picture. I shall have to take my palette out one day and paint them," said Elizabeth enjoying herself. "I never realised how much I missed riding."

To the left, Thomas pointed out the cliffs at Mavis Grind, saying he would take her there for a ride one day. "The countryside to the North is rocky but beautiful. There is a village up there called Hillswick and that is where my boats come in with merchandise. I have a booth there for storing goods also."

"Oh Thomas, look at the small booths set up along the shore here. They must be the temporary ones put up by the Dutchmen," Elizabeth exclaimed.

"Yes," agreed Thomas, "the German ones are built of stone, in Yell and Whalsay. They not only bring over requirements for fishing to store in them, but often material and furs which they import from Russia. I shall have to take you to the Whalsay one some day. It is fascinating," ended Thomas.

There was a strong smell of fish as they passed the booths. Drying in the sun, salted fish lay on large stones on the shore, or were tied together by the tails and hung over bars of wood stuck into the sand. If it rained, the fish were heaped on the beach and covered with tarpaulins.

Elizabeth wanted to know what the little stone buildings were with no windows or chimney and built with the stones not close together so that the wind blew into them. Thomas explained they were called skeos or houses where fish were dried by the wind blowing through the apertures in the walls. The fish were then called 'blawn fish'.

Passing the little jetty at Brae, Thomas drew his wife's attention to a Faroese boat which had just moored there. It was quite different to the Dutch 'busses' or German 'cogs' more the shape of the Shetland 'yoals', long and narrow actually pliable in the long run of the waves.

"There is not much of interest now till we get to Wethersta, just the moor road," said Thomas. "It is a fine old mansion house, not so outstanding as Busta House, I think, but then I am maybe prejudiced! I like the situation of Busta House. It is sheltered and gets a lot of sun, whereas Wethersta is built on the side of the hill overlooking the voe. It is very cold in winter getting the full blast of the south-westerly gales. I trust my cousin Andrew is at home now that we have ridden all this way!" he laughed.

Entering the open gates the couple rode round the side of the house to the stables.

"Ah, here is Gibbie the grieve. We shall leave the ponies in your good care," said Thomas dismounting, "Do you like Lady Busta's little mare?"

"She is splendid sir," answered Gibbie. "I will rub the ponies down and give them something to eat."

"Thank you," Thomas turned and helped Elizabeth to dismount.

"Come, we shall be in time for our afternoon tea," Thomas smiled, "their cook makes the most wonderful cakes."

Ringing the large bell-pull at the front door, the couple waited on the steps leading to the huge studded, wooden door. A maid opened it.

"Is Andrew Gifford at home?" asked Thomas.

"Yes sir," the girl answered, "Come this way please."

Taking their hats and gloves she placed them on the hall stand.

Opening a door off the hallway, she announced,

"Thomas Gifford and Lady Busta to see you."

Andrew and his wife rose up quickly.

"My, this is an honour," said Andrew, "we did not expect to see you today! You have surely travelled by horseback. We usually see your boat arrive, Thomas."

"You are right there," Thomas agreed. "I have bought a little mare for Elizabeth and knew she would enjoy the ride here. I came on Jasper. It was pleasant riding today and I was able to point out many different places of interest."

"It is quite a while since I rode last," Elizabeth told her host, "but I have really enjoyed it today, especially coming to visit you at Wethersta."

Andrew's wife rang the bell and when Maggie, the maid appeared, asked her to send in the afternoon tea.

The ladies chatted about the latest style of hats and dresses, while the men-folk talked about boats, fishing and the weather.

Tea was much appreciated, scones with home-made jam and lashings of cream, and a sponge made with finest flour and sifted sugar on top. The silver tea service sparkled and the china cups and saucers were of the most delicate Elizabeth had ever seen. Her hostess was rightly proud of her beautiful home.

"Thomas was telling me that Earl Robert Stewart built this house. It is lovely, quite magnificent. I have often been to Scalloway Castle, which his son Patrick built, but it is in sad disrepair," Elizabeth observed.

"Yes," answered Andrew, "But did you know that Lord Morton gave Sir Andrew, your brother permission to plunder the gateways and windows of Scalloway Castle, of their ornaments for his house at Sand?"

"I often wondered where they came from," smiled Elizabeth.

"Well," continued her hostess, "the castle was a beautiful building in its day. Scottish baronial style with handsome corbel towers. It is four storeys high with vaulted ceilings, and the kitchen has a well in it! The entry hall is spacious and the large windows are protected by iron gratings. Above the entry is a stone with the inscription

'That house whose foundation on a Rock shall stand -
But if on the sand it shall fall'.

When soldiers came to carry Patrick Stewart off for arrest, he hid in a secret chamber in a turret in the castle. He always smoked a pipe, this was his undoing! The soldiers saw the smoke of his tobacco coming out of one of the narrow slits and arrested him."

Andrew's wife suggested a walk in the garden.

"It is a lovely day," she commented to Elizabeth, "and the latest flowers I planted are coming out in bloom. Sometimes the little Dutch boats carry bulbs and I buy them in exchange for butter, eggs, even ornaments and animals. They are rare and very expensive. I think they called them tulips."

"We are planting a small hawthorn hedge at the back of the house," said Elizabeth, "to shelter the flowers on the sloping terrace below. The rowans have taken at the front, of which I am glad. Also the willows, down each side of the steps. We call it "The Willow Walk".

After studying the flowers and admiring the garden, the company made their way to the stables.

Thomas and Elizabeth thanked their host and hostess for a very pleasant afternoon, and mounted their ponies which Gibbie had ready. They all waved farewell.

"I have enjoyed our time there," said Elizabeth, "what a lovely couple and such a wonderful old house."

"Yes," Thomas agreed, "but I still prefer Busta."

Arriving back at the house James took charge of the ponies while the couple went into the house to have a rest after the long ride.

During dinner that evening Elizabeth told her husband she would like to have some 'tulips', she thought they were called, from the Dutch boats. Thomas enquired next day at one of the Dutch booths and they had a few left, and seeing they were for Master Gifford he could have them for half the usual price. Thomas bought them, thinking the price was exorbitant. Elizabeth was thrilled to receive them. She gave them to the gardener next day to plant and trusted they would blossom like the Wethersta ones.

Elizabeth took a great interest in the garden. The high walls surrounding it protected the trees and flowers from the blustery winds and sea breezes.

"How are the vegetables today?" she asked the gardener. "Can we have some for cook? Maybe turnips, carrots and parsnips. Put some herbs in also. The artichokes will do another time. I shall send Beth out to fetch them. The fruit trees have had a lot of sun lately so should be ripening. I shall get cook to make a gooseberry pie for dinner tonight. The currants are not quite ready yet, but those strawberries were delicious yesterday. We had strawberry jam at Wethersta so I must speak to cook about making some also."

"The potatoes are very good this year," said William, "in all, I think the garden has done well."

"Thanks to the gardener," smiled Elizabeth.

Chapter 3

THOMAS GOES FISHING

It was a lovely evening so Thomas and James set off with fishing rods, up over the hill to the nearby loch of Bayswater. Thomas enjoyed James' company, he always had some story to tell.

"I believe you are going to Lerwick soon, sir. You will no doubt visit the prison." said James smiling.

"Yes, James, I'm afraid so," answered Thomas. "There is always someone in the prison to see, or a quarrel to settle."

"I heard one story, sir, about the officer who came to inspect the prison in Lerwick. Going into the county jail he found it was empty. He saw a man outside washing the windows and asked him if he could tell him where the policeman was.

"Yes, sir, he has gone to Gulberwick for the day," was the reply.

"Could you please show me to the cell?" asked the officer. "I can speak to the prisoner myself."

"Oh, sir," replied the man, "I am the prisoner!!"

Thomas laughed. "That must have been a long time ago. I doubt if anyone would get away with it so easy these days."

All of a sudden his face became solemn – "I think I've got a fish James," he whispered, "and it's a beauty."

"I'd say about three pounds, sir," James replied.

Thomas landed the trout on the green bank and James unhooked it.

"Lady Busta will be pleased with her dinner tomorrow," said Thomas, casting his line into the loch again. "It takes time and patience, but it's good sport and very rewarding."

On their way back to the house Thomas asked James if he knew of anyone who would make a peat basket for him.

15

"Well, sir, I used to make them of an evening, before I came to work for you. Would you like me to make you one the same as you already have?" offered James.

"That would be splendid, James," answered Thomas. "Does your wife still keep the croft going and the family as well?"

"Yes, sir, I help all I can when I go home at night," replied James. "It's hard work, but I have two sons and they are a great help to my wife. I don't know what I will do when they are of an age to go to the fishing. There are six little ones to feed besides the old folks. My wife knits and also keeps hens and that brings in a little extra. I am honoured to work for you sir."

Lady Busta was indeed pleased to see the trout Thomas had caught. "We shall have a meal tomorrow night fit for a king," she said delighted.

As Thomas sat in his study next morning, a knock came to the door. Beth ushered James in.

"Well James, what can I do for you today?" asked his employer.

"Sir, I came to report the killing of a sea eagle. I was down at the shore at Mavis Grind collecting some driftwood and I saw it flying around so went home for my gun. I also killed two ravens and a crow."

"You did well James I shall put that on your pay sheet," said Thomas. "Let's see now, 1 Eagle 5/-, 2 Ravens 6p and 1 crow 2p. That all comes to five shillings and eight pence."

"I made a start to the basket last night," James informed him going out of the door.

Thomas tapped the weather-glass. Another fine day!

"Elizabeth, would you like to see the loch I caught the fish in last night? We can walk to the cairn on the top of the hill and see it from there." Thomas suggested.

"Can we go after lunch?" Elizabeth asked. "I seem to have such a lot to catch up on today. Beth is taking off early to help in the hay and will not be back till late afternoon. She is a good worker. Her mother has quite a handful with their little croft and all the children to feed."

"Certainly, my dear," replied Thomas, "maybe I should suggest the same to James as I don't need him till later on. He was telling me yesterday about his two boys helping his wife. We are so fortunate to have such willing workers. I will go and tell him now."

James was exceedingly grateful and he made his way home as quickly as he could, surprising his wife who was all set to do the task of building the big hay stack in their yard, with the help of the boys.

After lunch, Elizabeth put on her walking boots and, taking a stick, joined Thomas on their walk up the hill to the cairn. Taking long, easy strides they soon reached the top.

Turning round they looked down on Busta House and the lands adjoining, then across to Brae and further down the voe to Wethersta.

"I think it is such lovely scenery here." Elizabeth shouted above the wind to her husband.

Someone repeated exactly what she had just said! Elizabeth got quite a shock and she hung onto Thomas' arm. He laughed.

"That is your own voice echoing," he said, and shouted something also, which came back as clear as anything.

"I had a visit from James this morning," Thomas told Elizabeth, "last night he killed a sea eagle, two ravens and a crow. They are always attacking the sheep and lambs. There are many birds nesting in the heather up here, there is a lark over there and a curlew. There is a hawk flying above us. When Robert and Patrick Stewart lived in Shetland the falconer of the Royal household requisitioned a fowl from each house in every parish. After the king tired of the amusement, the falconer no longer had to collect the levy. In fact, he brought to the island some weasels to destroy the hens."

Chapter 4

ELIZABETH'S SECRET

B usta Voe was a busy place with all the local and foreign commerce going on. This was good for trade but often resulted in quarrels, fights and theft. Head Courts were held twice a year when Thomas Gifford presided. He also held an Annual Court in different parishes.

Business again necessitated Thomas leaving Busta.

"You will be all right?" he questioned Elizabeth. "You have been looking a bit tired lately. Take things easy, my dear."

The day after Thomas left for Lerwick, Beth brought Lady Busta her morning cup of tea.

"Good morning Ma'am," she said cheerfully pulling back the heavy curtains. "What a lovely day."

Hearing a moan, Beth turned to see her Ladyship lying white-faced on the bed. She got quite a shock, as her mistress usually greeted her equally as cheerfully.

"Ma'am are you all right?" she asked.

"No, Beth, I feel so sick. I've felt like this for a couple of days now, but today I cannot lift my head off the pillow. Please fetch Martha," moaned Elizabeth.

"Yes, Ma'am," Beth ran down the stairs to the kitchen.

"Martha, Martha, you've got to go to her Ladyship at once. I think she's gyann tae cry." (Shetland for pregnant).

"Don't talk like that in this house," scolded Martha, "and don't breathe a word of that to anyone else."

For days now Martha had seen the tell-tale signs, but kept it to herself.

"Ma'am," she said gently entering Elizabeth's room, "you are not feeling too well today, Beth tells me."

"Martha you are the only one I can confide in here. You are a woman of integrity and I trust you wholly. Tell me, am I very ill? What can I do? I feel so sick."

"Now, now," Martha soothed her, "if you will drink up your tea while it is hot and eat the biscuit, you will feel a lot better. I shall keep some breakfast hot for you."

"I couldn't eat breakfast feeling like this," Lady Busta retorted.

"No, Ma'am," Martha explained patiently, "but you will feel better after your tea".

"Very well," conceded her Ladyship somewhat petulantly, "but tell me please, is there something dreadfully wrong with me?"

"Well," began Martha slowly, reluctant to tell her mistress.

"Tell me," shouted Elizabeth scaring the poor woman.

"You're gyaan tae cry," Martha blurted out, then realised what she had said.

Elizabeth smiled. "Cry?" she said in a quizzical tone. "But why should I cry? I only feel sick."

"Sorry Ma'am, I should have said... have said.." stammered Martha.

"Said what?" asked Elizabeth gently, this time, "Don't keep me in suspense."

"You are maybe 'in the family way' as we say here," she answered.

"In the family way," repeated her mistress slowly, "I see – you think I may be having a family then? But Martha, that is wonderful. Please keep this to yourself, will you?" she pleaded.

Nodding her head, Martha said, "Your breakfast is waiting," and went out, closing the door behind her.

Elizabeth sat up in bed, no longer feeling sick, but elated at the thought that she was carrying Thomas' child. She lay back on the pillows and gave a little sigh of happiness.

On returning home again, Thomas was glad to see his wife looking a lot happier than when he left, and with a bit more colour in her cheeks.

Elizabeth wondered when she would be able to tell the exciting news to Thomas – these things were just not discussed in their circle! He would have to know soon though, as she wanted the little room at the top of the stairs made into a nursery. A nurse would have to be employed and come up from the Mainland. There were clothes and baby furniture to think of too.

Next time Thomas mentioned Lerwick, Elizabeth said, "I shall come with you as I have several things to buy."

"All right, my dear," agreed the surprised Thomas. "We shall go on Friday.

Cook made a picnic basket ready in case they felt hungry on the way.

James rowed them in the boat to Olnafirth and they hired ponies as far as Catfirth and joined the boat there for Lerwick.

Elizabeth was feeling more like herself now and enjoyed the journey.

"This is great," said Thomas, "it is lonely travelling on my own. It will do you good to get away from the house for a day."

"I am looking forward to seeing the shops again," Elizabeth smiled. "Do you mind if I do some shopping on my own?" she blushed!

"Of course not," her unsuspecting husband replied. "We can meet up at the hotel for a meal. There is no hurry as we are staying overnight there."

Elizabeth had asked advice of Martha as to what would be best to buy for the baby, the list did not seem much but once all the little things were gathered together they made quite a fair-sized parcel.

Next day proved to be fine and as soon as Thomas and Elizabeth arrived at Olnafirth there was James to meet them.

Martha helped to store away the baby clothes when the couple arrived home.

"You will need to tell the Master soon," she advised one day, "before anyone else guesses your secret."

Chapter 5

MARGARET ARRIVES

Thomas Gifford had had an exacting day. He was tired and things had not gone according to plan. The salt had not arrived for the fish, the men were awkward and on the whole he was glad of the peace and quiet of the house in the evening.

"Thomas?" queried Elizabeth after dinner. "I have some news for you."

"Not just now, Elizabeth," he said churlishly, "I'll hear it later."

"But.. but it is something important," she began again.

"It will have to wait," he bellowed and left the room.

Elizabeth was shaken, she had never seen her husband in a mood like this before. She would certainly keep her secret to herself.

Next day Thomas had cooled down a trifle.

"What were you going to tell me yesterday?" he asked impatiently.

"Oh, nothing I can't tell you again," said Elizabeth haughtily. I can play the same game as you she thought!

Speaking to Martha next day, Elizabeth plucked up the courage to ask her – "Martha, you have had children of your own, will you please tell me what happens. I know it seems ridiculous that I do not know, but I would like you to give me the details. It's not our custom to speak of such things and I want to be ready. Please do not spare any details," she added.

"It is customary to have our children delivered by a howdie," began Martha nervously.

"A what?" asked Elizabeth.

"That is the name we give a woman who is at the birth. I used to do the job often before I came here to work."

"Martha what can you not do?" laughed Elizabeth relieved.

"But Ma'am you will have a private nurse and a doctor. The nurse will stay till you are on your feet again."

"Tell me what happens at the actual birth, I am so frightened."

"Do not be frightened Ma'am, it is the most natural thing in the world.." Martha proceeded to tell her Ladyship about childbirth.

"I will not worry if you are about," sighed Elizabeth.

......

Thomas Gifford appointed a local artist – one John Irvine – to make oil paintings of himself and his wife.

"I want them to hang together in the drawing-room. Just the two of us," he said giving Elizabeth a hug.

"What were you going to tell me the other night love?" he queried. "I am sorry I did not listen, and it seemed so important to you. I had a very pressing issue on my mind which had to be cleared next day."

"It could not have been as important as my news though," Elizabeth smiled up to him. "We are to have a family." she blushed.

Thomas looked at his wife, then held her at arms length.

"You mean," he stammered, "you mean, you are in the family way?"

"Yes, Thomas." she replied.

Taking Elizabeth in his arms he held her tight.

"That is wonderful, my dear, you will have to look after yourself very carefully now," he added lovingly.

"Remember that shopping trip to Lerwick?" she laughed. "That was the baby's clothes I was buying. I was so excited."

"My darling, to think I could have heard this news days ago. Will you forgive me?" he said kissing her.

"Yes, this time." she replied.

"What about a perambulator and a rocking horse?" began Thomas, but Elizabeth just laughed and said, "There will be time for them later."

Preparations went ahead for the baby's arrival. The nursery was the first priority, then the nurse came from the Mainland. She was a strict person and she and Martha did not always see eye to eye. Beth was always getting scolded for something, and on the whole everyone wished that the baby would come soon so that they could all get on with their lives in peace again!

Elizabeth was very tired and feeling the weight of the baby heavy. She too longed for its safe arrival but with a hint of trepidation.

What if anything went wrong with the birth?

What if the baby was not perfect?

Would she manage to feed it all right?

Would it be a boy or a girl?

She would love a little girl herself, to dress in sweet frilly frocks but she knew Thomas wanted a boy, a son and heir, to take round his estate to help him in his tremendous workload.

Quite suddenly, she felt a searing pain across her back. She rang the bell for the nurse.

"It is nothing, go to sleep again," commanded the woman disappearing out of the door.

Ringing the bell again, Martha appeared, and Elizabeth burst into tears.

"I had a bad pain in my back", she sobbed, "and nurse is so unsympathetic."

"I'll get you a hot cup of tea, that will soothe you," consoled Martha.

Taking in the tea, Martha propped her mistress into a sitting position and handed her the cup and saucer.

"Stay with me a while Martha," she pleaded, "I am so frightened."

Lying back on the pillow again, she suddenly sat up and cried out in pain.

"Get up and walk about," said Martha, which Elizabeth did, and the pain eased off.

"Where is nurse?" she asked.

Martha shrugged her shoulders. "Gone for a walk."

Nurse had certainly gone for a long walk, it was three hours before she returned, and to her horror Elizabeth was in the second stage of labour. Things began to move fast, and although nurse was a hard person she certainly knew her work. The baby was soon born.

"It's a girl," said nurse.

"Is she all right?" queried Elizabeth falteringly, half afraid to speak.

"Of course she is," was the curt reply.

It was a while before Elizabeth was comfortable again and Thomas allowed in to see her and the baby.

Thomas was overjoyed and kept telling his wife how well she had done.

"We shall call her Margaret," said Elizabeth. "Our first child, this will be a year to remember – 1715."

Martha came with a cup of tea and was happy to see the little one. She presented her with the most beautiful, delicate lace shawl Elizabeth had ever seen.

"Oh Martha, this is magnificent, it must have taken you weeks to do this."

"I spun the wool myself Ma'am," she said proudly.

"I shall treasure it," Elizabeth said with tears in her eyes. "Thank you Martha for all you have done for me." she whispered.

"It's a pleasure Ma'am." Martha was as relieved as anyone to see the perfect little baby lying asleep in her cot.

It was a few weeks after this till the nurse left Busta House and things were back to normal. Each time Martha or Beth heard a footstep they cringed as they expected to hear the stentorious voice of nurse!

The nursemaid employed at the time stayed on and eventually became one of the household helps. She was a pleasant girl and a real help to Elizabeth, especially at feeding times.

Elizabeth loved Margaret with all her heart. She was beautiful and her very own. She was also a good baby and had the best of everything. She grew up to love and obey her parents.

Chapter 6

THE CROFTERS

Three years later, Elizabeth began to feel the symptoms of childbirth again. She kept it secret as long as she could, then told Martha.

"As you would say Martha, "I think I'm going to 'cry' again!" and she laughed! "It seems a long time now since the day you told me that. I was so frightened, but feel better about it this time."

"Yes, Ma'am you did well, but I do hope they send another nurse this time!"

Elizabeth set her heart on having a little son, and, much to her delight, when the time came, she gave birth to a sturdy boy, whom Thomas named John.

Margaret was a sweet-natured girl and her mother loved her, but John was her favourite – and always would be.

Another little girl arrived three years later, Elizabeth, then Ann. Robert was born in 1726, then Thomas, but he did not survive.

In 1729 Francis Patrick arrived. In 1730 William was born, then Christina, and in 1733, Hay. Later Thomas, James, Barbara and lastly Andrina.

There were fourteen children born to the couple altogether.

......

As John grew older, his father would take him in the gig to the bustling head of Busta Voe where he was going to see some new machinery or boat that had been bought. He felt it was never soon enough for his son and heir to be able to think out transactions which would bring in the necessary money to buy more goods or land.

John loved going with his father and meeting the cosmopolitan band of men around the little harbour. Some wore baggy trousers with wooden clogs. Some, strange hats and coats! The men too enjoyed seeing the boy, he reminded them of their own families back home.

27

"Father," said John one lovely, summer morning, "I see the merchants from Bremen have arrived, they must have come yesterday. Their booths are set up, and if we don't go soon we shall not be able to get near. People hear about their arrival and buy up all the best things. Come on."

"Yes, yes," chided Thomas, "sit and finish your breakfast first. We shall have to see James about getting butter and eggs for the men. I believe we have a surfeit of milk meantime, the cows having calved recently. We also have oil from the whales caught in the Voe and a quantity of dried, salted fish and herring."

"Elizabeth, could you arrange for Bertha to collect as many knitted goods as she can from the crofters and we will barter them for tar for the roofs, lines, and hooks for the fishing. Not forgetting my special tobacco and spirits. Most of all we need salt to cure the fish. We will pay some things in money, but I want to keep plenty for the Orkney boats, they are short of money, when they bring oats, corn and cloth, which we desperately need."

......

Thomas, being the kindly man he was, loved to buy presents for his family. Passing a field of Shetland ponies while out for a walk, John stopped to talk to them. A little piebald one came up and licked his hand. John was thrilled.

"Father," he shouted, "do you think I could have this little pony for my own?"

"Well," his father drawled, "we shall have to see about that. I will need to ask James about him."

"Will you do that Father? I should love to ride like you and Mother," he finished.

When James was asked to make the pony available for John to ride, he readily agreed, and so it was that John had his first riding lesson. James not only taught the boy to ride, but to saddle his own pony, groom him properly, clean his stall and feed him.

John and Gypsy got on well together.

The children grew up in a wonderful home, with a loving father and strict mother. Thomas was a good father to his large family and a devoted, indulgent husband, a staunch friend, a good, amiable, sensible and religious man.

As the boys grew older they went with their father to the booths and market place at Brae. The girls would sit in the sitting-room with their mother where they were taught to sew or embroider.

Thomas Gifford, besides being a shrewd business man, was careful for the health of the men on his boats. After being cramped up in the boats for days at sea, he felt they needed some exercise.

28

In the field behind the booth, he kept a number of Shetland ponies. When the men, and some of the Dutchmen too, came ashore they would come to the field. Handing over a 'stiver' they were given a pony to ride. A young boy would lead them around the field, sometimes they had races.

The Busta children enjoyed watching them but were never allowed to join in. Each child had a wooden hoop and a stick with which they propelled it along. It kept them outside in the fresh air, and also gave them exercise.

Inside, they played hide-and-seek in the corridors.

It was quite a different life for the families outside Busta House.

The families being very poor, each member had to give a helping hand, however young. The father and boys, seventeen to seventy, were forced to go to the fishing. There were no exceptions other than those who were sick or old. This being the staple industry, prices paid were very low.

Three pence a ling, 1p a cod, 5 shillings for a barrel of herring.

Many of the fishermen returning from long, weary hours at sea were glad to get home to help on the small croft again and be with their families. Others spent their pay on drink.

The women at home toiled all day, with cows to feed and milk, butter to make, hens to feed and gather eggs, peats to cut and dry and cart home, food to make for the family, potatoes and vegetables to plant and care for, corn to sow and harvest. Besides all this they were pregnant a lot of the time, nursing babies and bringing up children. It was indeed a very hard life.

In the evenings the men would sit and smoke (if they could afford it), while making baskets for the peats and hay to be carried in.

The women, after a busy day's toil, sat down to spin wool and knit the coarse stockings bought by the Dutchmen. The finer wool was made into shawls, scarves, jumpers, hats.

The young girls were employed caarding and spinning as well. Sometimes the men knitted also.

The fiddle (violin) was a 'must' in every home. The first one to finish his basket would fetch down the fiddle and play a tune or two, feet tapping to the music. The chief night was 'John's Mass', in June, before the fishing began.

The barn was cleared at Busta House and all the village folks gathered for a 'barn dance'. There were items, songs, recitations, stories and dances. Each person brought home-made bannocks (scones), butter and some milk, also a peat for the fire.

If the fishing season was good, the families still lived frugally trying to put a little past for the winter months.

However, in the stormy seas many a boat was lost and a whole village lost its men. These were sad occasions for it left the woman of the house to cope alone. At these times, neighbours rallied round and helped whenever they could, unless they too had been robbed of their men folks.

Some were fortunate to have work on estates, such as the grieve at Busta, the farm workers and boatmen on the ferries. Cooks, personal maids and scullery maids were fortunate to be employed as well.

Chapter 7

SMALLPOX

In 1740 the dreaded smallpox reached Shetland. Lady Busta was thankful that her dear John was safely away on business in Germany, but she trusted that none of the family would catch it.

Some weeks after the knowledge of its arrival, three of the children became unwell and the old family doctor was called in. He diagnosed smallpox. Elizabeth was beside herself with worry. Betty and Frankie became quite ill and a nurse was installed in the house for the duration of the illness. Thomas, jnr. complained of feeling unwell, as did Barbara, and within a few days all the children were affected.

Betty, being now nineteen, was very ill indeed, and Frankie only eleven had taken it badly too.

Thomas Gifford sat at his desk, head in hands, distraught. He re-read again the entries in his diary.

"July 5th -   Poor Betty and Frankie took to the bed yesterday.
July 10th - Pox spots out – Betty and Frankie very bad. The pox riseth slowly.
July 12th - The bairns are worse.
July 13th - Thursday...the bairns very bad all day, feverish and weak.
July 14th - Little easier – extreme weak, pox begins to fall.
July 15th - Saturday...the bairns very weak and sore, but some hope.
July 18th - My dear Betty died about 7 in a very calm manner.
Robbie lay all day.
July 19th - Wednesday...Poor Frankie died about 7pm very calm.
July 21st - The pox began to appear on Robbie and Christie. They lay all day.
The bairns were buried. Andrina took to the bed.

31

July 25th - Tuesday...Hay took to the bed – all the bairns uneasy, but blessed be God not very ill. Robbie better again.

July 26th - The bairns continue pretty easy – few pox appear on them but begin to rise."

Lady Busta came in the door, and, seeing her husband so distressed put her hand on his shoulder.

"What can we do?" she asked distraught. "There's James, Barbara and Thomas in bed now."

"Commit them to God, that is all we can do," he answered.

"He cannot take these as well," shrieked Elizabeth.

"The Lord hath given, the Lord hath taken away, blessed be the Name of the Lord," quoted Thomas.

Elizabeth turned and went out of the door furious. The iron had entered her soul!

Thomas looked at the pages longingly again. How he loved each one of the children. He had given them his own pet names! Elizabeth was called Betty, Francis was Frankie, Robert, Robbie and Christina was Christie.

Betty had been a lovely girl and a real help to her mother. They would sit and sew or read together. She was beautiful in looks too.

Frankie at eleven was at an interesting age. So eager to learn with his tutor.

Robbie, Christie and Andrina survived the smallpox. But James, Barbara and Thomas, his name-sake, although nursed carefully, finally gave in to the fell disease.

If it had not been for the return of John from Hamburg in a few days time, Elizabeth would definitely have gone under. She could not be comforted or helped in any way. Thomas, grieving silently, had many a difficult day.

......

Thomas wished his children to have a proper education, and sixteen years previously had called a meeting of the heritors and chief men of the district together to discuss the matter in which various districts could have their own school.

The Shetland gentry were all agreed on this proposal. As their children grew older they were sent to Lerwick where one or two teachers taught subjects such as English, navigation, writing. For further education, pupils had to leave the islands and reside in Scotland.

The proposal did eventually come about, but sadly, not in Thomas Gifford's lifetime.

Chapter 8

"BARBARA AND ELISE"

A young lad had been employed to help the gardener as each year new trees and flowers were planted. An ornamental garden in an enclosed area needed attention. Here Lady Busta liked to sit with a book or her embroidery on a fine day.

Malcolm was a hard worker. Beth was often sent to the kitchen garden to fetch vegetables for cook. She and Malcolm struck up a friendship which was to be lasting. As Beth would enter the gate in the high wall, Malcolm took her basket from her and filled it ready to take back to the kitchen. He also helped her to carry the heavy basket with eggs which she collected from the hen-house in the field up the hill.

One evening as Beth was going a message for Lady Busta, she stumbled on a loose stone and fell, hurting her ankle. Unable to walk, she sat for a while wondering what to do. At that moment, Malcolm, who had been out exercising Jasper, happened to come by. He lifted Beth onto the horse and took her to the house. He carried her into the kitchen where Martha bathed and bandaged the ankle.

When Martha left the room, Malcolm plucked up courage and asked Beth if she would meet him some evening after their work and they could go for a walk. Beth was shy at first, but agreed. And so their friendship grew.

Whilst out one evening Malcolm shyly asked Beth what her answer would be if he asked her to marry him?

"I would be deeply touched," she said in a whisper.

"Well, let's set a date," said Malcolm quickly.

"I will have to ask permission from her Ladyship to leave her employment first," answered Beth, "and what time would suit her."

Beth had grown used to her mistresses curt orders and thankless tasks. Intuitively prepared for each situation she felt ready to cope. However, she had not anticipated her Ladyship's answer to her question this time.

"Come in," shouted Lady Busta as Beth timidly knocked on the sitting-room door. "And what is it you want, girl, I did not ring for you."

"No, Ma'am," whispered Beth shaking at the knees. "I have come to ask permission to leave your employment here as I am to get married soon."

"What?" roared Lady Busta unable to believe her ears. "You going to leave? certainly NOT. Who would do the many things you do for me each day? You know EXACTLY what I want and I could not train another girl now."

"But Ma'am," began Beth.

"That is quite enough," said Lady Busta, "now fetch my afternoon tea."

Beth arrived in the kitchen in such a state that Martha had to make the tea and take it to Madam herself.

"And what, may I ask, has happened to my servant?" said Lady Busta haughtily.

"She is upset Ma'am because you will not consent to her leaving to get married," answered Martha.

"Is she now? We'll soon put a stop to her nonsense. Bring the girl here," she ordered.

As Martha left the room, Lady Busta began to wonder what she would have done if Beth had not been such a wonderful help to her. Maybe she was being a bit hard on her. She knew she would never get anyone to equal Beth again.

As Beth knocked and entered the room a second time, her Ladyship was quite upset to see the change in the girl. She looked pale and had obviously been crying sorely.

"I shall consider your request Beth," she conceded, "you have been a faithful servant to me, but I should like you to stay here until I can get someone suitable to replace you. You may go now." Lady Busta sat back in her chair trying to think of anyone whom she could contact.

......

The Pitcairns were related to the Giffords and Lady Busta was aware that the family was miserably poorly off. She had an idea.

That evening after dinner as everyone gathered in the drawing-room to talk over the day's happenings, she drew her husband's attention to the fact that their relations, the Pitcairns, were in a bad position, and she was wondering if it would be possible to adopt the two girls as protègès into the household.

Thomas Gifford pulled hard on his pipe, eyebrows knit together, a scowl on his face, then he reflected;

Elizabeth had lost two girls in the smallpox episode and was maybe feeling that these girls' company would be appreciated. He replied,

"Well, my dear, you know best, you have grieved long for your two girls, I know. Maybe having Barbara and Elise in the house will help bring back some happiness to you again."

Apart from giving the girls a home, Lady Busta was shrewd enough to see into the future – she would also have a girl to wait on her when Beth left her position.

No time was spared in writing a letter to Mrs. Pitcairn offering to adopt the girls, which, incidentally would prove a help to herself emotionally as she still mourned the loss of Betty and Barbara, so recently taken from her. At the same time, she, Lady Busta, would be able to give Barbara and Elise the upbringing they would need for the future, also the education they lacked.

On receiving the letter, Mrs Pitcairn, who was a widow, wrote back at once to Lady Busta, thanking her for her great kindness in thinking to adopt the two girls and educate them along with her own family.

If Mrs Pitcairn had known what the outcome of her letter was to be, she would have gladly kept her two dear girls at home, and at least given them the love they deserved.

Once Lady Busta received the letter thanking her for her kindness and generosity, it did not take that lady long to get Martha to put a room ready for the two sisters. Having lived frugally for some time, Lady Busta was not about to give them her best, so they were allocated a small room in the attic.

On the day the girls arrived, they were welcomed by Martha who showed them to their room. It was sparsely furnished, but the girls did not mind. They were together, and at first it seemed quite an adventure. Barbara was about twelve years of age and her sister was younger.

Both girls were brought to the sitting-room where Lady Busta sat drinking tea.

"Come and sit down," she ordered when they were ushered into the room, "you have both come here to stay in our household and I trust we shall get on well together. Any orders I give will be obeyed immediately. At meal-times, in the dining room, I expect you to be punctual and impeccably dressed. You will keep your own room tidy and cleaned and I will see to it that you are included in the lessons each day given by the Reverend John Fisken. There is also a music teacher, Mr William Troop, and you will be given dancing lessons by him.

"We have prayers in the morning after breakfast, and you are expected to attend. Martha will show you the rooms now. Ring the bell," she ordered.

Once in the corridor the girls began to giggle nervously.

"Don't worry about her bark, it's worse than her bite," Martha reassured them.

That evening, before dinner, the two girls dressed in their finest frocks and brushed and curled each other's hair. Barbara, a brunette, was a slim very attractive girl with brown eyes and a lovely smile. Elise was smaller with blonde hair and large blue eyes.

They arrived at the dining room just as Thomas Gifford and his wife were about to enter. Standing aside, they waited till all the family had trooped in, then followed them into the room. They stood awkwardly waiting to be shown their seats.

Martha, as ever, saw the situation and led each girl to her respective seat. When Thomas Gifford and Lady Busta sat down, the family did so also.

All bowed heads as the 'Master' said 'Grace'.

"So these are the additions to our family," boomed Thomas. Both girls blushed.

"No need to be shy now," he laughed, "it's good to see another two lasses at the table again. What do you say my dear?" and he looked at Elizabeth who smiled.

"Now tell me your names," he said.

Barbara, pointing to her sister said, "My sister is Elise and I am Barbara."

"Good," shouted Thomas, "I shall call you Babbie and Alice!"

Lady Busta smiled. She was just wondering how she could ever get used to calling this girl Barbara, after losing her own daughter of the same name so short a while before.

The two girls settled in well at Busta House. George Pitcairn, their father, had been a wealthy man. He had owned his own brig and was captain of her. His brother, a very prosperous landowner, lived in the island of Unst, at Muness.

Mrs Pitcairn came from the landed gentry also and was a descendant of the knight Laurence Bruce of Cultmalendie. He built Muness Castle in Unst.

Chapter 9

GIFFORD's BOATS

Besides owning a large estate Thomas Gifford acted as Chamberlain in Shetland to the Earl of Morton, who was then in possession of the landed property and other duties of the Earldom of Orkney and Lordship of Zetland.

Thomas decided to write an historical description of the Shetland Islands in 1733. Only a man in Gifford's position could have had the knowledge he possessed about the laws, institutions, customs and nature of which existed at that time. Many customs had been handed down from the Scandinavian period before Shetland and Orkney were given to Britain as a dowry.

As Gifford travelled extensively throughout the islands in connection with his court work, he observed the conditions in which the people lived, and the food they produced or sold. He also took note of the people's names, their dialect, religions and superstitions.

The book included chapters on the government of Zetland, property transactions and Crown rents.

By the year 1740, Thomas Gifford was a wealthy, prosperous man. He was a good landlord and his employees respected him. He studied the interests of his tenants and dependants and went out of his way to help them.

Every available minute Thomas could find, apart from his work, was taken up with writing the manuscripts of his journal. Unfortunately something had to suffer and it was the family. More time spent with them might have brought out the best in them, but that was not to be, so wrapped up was he in his own thoughts.

......

Thomas Gifford owned boats and sometimes John was sent to Germany on one to do business with the merchants there. As he arrived in Lübeck, the first German port on the North Sea, he was fascinated to see the old city built in 1143. Salt warehouses lined part of the river. John had to order salt from these warehouses to cure the Shetland fish, Lübeck was a Hanseatic town. Germans had formed the Hanseatic League to protect their trade and exclude outsiders. They formed guilds which eventually came under the control of their home town.

John made his way along the cobbled stone street on the waterfront, passing by horses and carts with their varied loads.

Arriving at the Seaman's Guild House for sailors, captains and shipowners (since 1535), John went up the steps into the nicely kept house. Making a reservation for a room, he was taken upstairs to a nice clean bedroom and provided with water to wash. A meal downstairs awaited him.

John left the House again and walked past a huge Gothic church, then the Rathus (Town Hall), and on to the market square. There seemed to be the smell of beer everywhere! Every town had a brewery and exported their beer to ports in Scandinavia and towns in the Baltic. Seeing a large barge tie up at the pier, John watched as it was unloaded.

The canal had replaced the old wagon-trails, making it economical to move bulk goods between East and West Europe. Foodstuffs and raw materials mostly made up the cargoes. Grain and flour from Poland, timber and iron from Sweden, candle wax and furs from Russia. Lübeck provided salt and from the Rhineland ports, wine and pottery. England provided woollen and linen cloth.

Some of these wares were brought to Shetland in the German cogs and stored in the Hanseatic booths, in Whalsay, South Mid Yell and Burra Voe.

......

It was with great excitement that the news of ships returning to Hillswick and elsewhere for Thomas Gifford, was greeted. So anxious was the Laird to see that the shipments had arrived safely and intact, that he himself, along with his boys, would wait eagerly for the boats to come ashore from the ships, and help to unload them.

There were boxes containing tea, a great luxury for Lady Busta, and sugar. Then bottles of water, for health reasons, and Thomas' favourite tobacco. Most important were the bags of salt for curing the fish, lines and hooks and many things needed for replacement for the fishing season.

Sealed bags of money were precious as Gifford had to pay his men. When money was scarce the men had to be paid in 'kind', or goods given in different commodities in equal value to the money. If the fishermen were not paid there were disastrous results as the tenants could not afford to buy corn and the other things needed to keep their meagre crofts going.

Slow-going sailing boats, the only means of transport, used by Gifford to obtain his purchases, plied between Hamburg, Spain, Denmark, Norway, Sweden and Leith, on the 'continent of Britain'.

Shetland fishermen used six or eight-oared boats in the home waters. Going to the 'Far Haaf' (deep sea), meant sailing out to sea until only the high land was sighted. In the boats were places to hold peats for a fire, a huge pot for boiling their fish to eat, home-made bannocks (scones) milk and water, and storage room for the fish they caught. Sometimes these boats were caught in a severe storm and did not return home. It was hard times for the women never knowing if their fathers, husbands, brothers or sons would return to them again.

After all the toil and danger, when the men eventually grounded their boats on the shingly shore, half of their catch had to be given to the Laird.

When pulling the boats up from the sea, huge halibut were placed on the beach and the boats drawn up over them to their 'noost' or place of safety further up at the banks. In the winter, the boats had noosts in the field above the beach. Long, narrow holes the shape of the boat were cut in the ground and the boat secured there.

While the men were at sea, the women did all the work on the crofts. Peats which had dried during the summer had to be taken home in panniers on the backs of little Shetland ponies. Being sturdy and strong they could carry very heavy loads.

Hay-making time was a pleasure in the warm, sunny days of summer, when the children helped too. Several crofters got together to help each other to bring it home.

The women knitted at all times. Going to and from the fields their hands were never idle. They carried small metal 'wires' or needles with a ball of wool and made a sock or glove as they walked along. These articles brought in a little money or were bartered for necessary goods. Larger garments were knitted while sitting at the fire at home. A leather sheath strapped round the waist was used to secure or hold the needle firm while knitting at great speed. The children had to be looked after and fed and many a large family depended on their upbringing from the older members of the family. In most homes, the old grandparents, if spared, spent their last days in the over-crowded house too. The grandmother would look after the infant in the cradle, rocking it with her foot, while she taught the older girls to knit. The old grandfather taught the boys to make things from wood and repair the croft implements.

Chapter 10

THE LACE HOSE

John, the oldest son, took an instant liking to Barbara and, with each passing day could not take his eyes off her. She was small and dainty with a lovely complexion. Always neatly dressed and well spoken, she had a superior air about her. It is maybe no wonder that John's thoughts strayed often towards this beautiful girl. He was now a man of twenty-eight or so, and she, a maiden of some fourteen years. A man of his age and position was usually married with a family of his own.

One day Lady Busta caught John speaking to Barbara. He had put a hand on her shoulder to point out of the window at some object in the distance across the water.

"Take your hand off the girl's shoulder," ordered Lady Busta sternly, "that is no way to behave in this house. Leave the room at once girl."

"Yes," whispered Barbara retiring and wondering why her Ladyship was so annoyed.

When John told his mother he was very fond of Barbara, she nearly collapsed!

......

One day when cook came for her interview, Lady Busta asked her if she knew where she might obtain a pair of ladies fine-knitted lace hose (stockings).

"Yes, Ma'am," answered Cook, "I can get a pair for you by tomorrow, if that is suitable."

After dinner next evening, cook produced the pair of knitted hose.

"And how much are these?" asked the ever-cautious lady!

They are generally sold for around 35/- Ma'am," replied cook.

"A bit expensive, don't you think?" asked her Ladyship "but they are certainly exquisitely made. May I ask who knitted them?" she questioned, obviously impressed.

"Well, Ma'am," Harriet hesitated.

"Come on," coaxed Elizabeth, "she must be quite an expert!"

"Yes, Ma'am she is," she replied, not sure whether to give the knitter's name away or not.

"If you don't tell me, I shall find out for myself," laughed Elizabeth.

"It's – it's Barbara, Ma'am," cook blurted out.

"Barbara? Barbara Pitcairn?"

"Yes, Ma'am," whispered Harriet, upset that she had given the girl's identity away.

"Bring her here at once," ordered Lady Busta.

Harriet disappeared to the kitchen where she found Barbara and Martha discussing a new lace pattern.

"Barbara, I've done something terrible! You'll never forgive me," she sobbed.

"Whatever has happened," asked a curious Barbara as she went over and put a comforting arm around cook.

"I had to tell her Ladyship it was you who knitted the hose," said cook, "and now she wants to see you."

"Don't worry about that," consoled the girl. "She was bound to find out in time. If you had not told her, someone else would have."

"I only hope you do not get into any trouble over it though," sobbed cook.

"It can't be that bad," assured Barbara as she left the room.

When the girl entered the drawing-room door, Lady Busta was holding the stockings in her hand.

"Am I to believe that you knitted these garments yourself? or was cook just trying to make you out to be cleverer than you are?" asked her Ladyship sarcastically.

"You are correct in assuming I made the hose, Ma'am" replied Barbara.

"I see," contemplated Lady Busta, "and do you think I believe a word of it?"

"I not only knitted the stockings, but spun the wool also," added the girl indignantly.

"Who taught you this craft, and when?" asked the astonished woman.

"Martha, Ma'am. I usually go down to the kitchen after dinner, instead of intruding on your family privacy here," said Barbara defensively.

"Ring the bell for Martha," ordered Elizabeth.

Martha appeared at the door ready for a lecture.

"You rang Ma'am?" she said.

"Tell me," began Elizabeth, "did you teach Barbara to spin and knit."

"Yes, Ma'am," was the reply.

"I see, I thought cook was maybe mistaken," said Lady Busta defending herself.

"Barbara collects the 'oo', sorry, Ma'am, the raw wool from the field then spins and knits it herself. She is quite an expert," added Martha.

"Does she possess a spinning wheel?" was the next question.

"Yes, Ma'am," replied Martha, "I gave her my mother's one. It has been in my family for many years, and I knew Barbara would treasure it."

"Barbara," Elizabeth said, turning to the girl, "go and fetch some of your 'oo', as you call it, and let me see you performing the operation from wool to stockings."

"Yes, Ma'am," Barbara disappeared from the room, with Martha at her heels.

"Thomas, I don't believe a word the girl is saying," accused Elizabeth peevishly, "she was never taught to knit that I know of."

"Betty, Betty, you are so hard on the poor girl," remonstrated Thomas, "give her a chance."

Barbara appeared again holding a box with wool and needles and Martha, with the spinning wheel.

"Sit near me," ordered Elizabeth, "so that I can see what you are doing, Barbara. Whatever are those for?" she questioned as Barbara took two pieces of wood from the box.

"These are cairders, Ma'am," explained the girl, "the two pieces of wood have small metal nails in one side of each – a quantity of wool is placed on one of the boards, and teased with the other to remove any grass or turf, then the wool becomes quite smooth."

"Put on your apron," advised Martha.

After a few minutes, her Ladyship asked to feel the teased wool. "It is beautifully soft," she agreed.

Rolling the wool between the backs of the two cairders, Barbara formed a 'rower' ready for spinning.

"Can you really spin?" the still unbelieving woman asked.

"Yes, Ma'am."

Barbara was not to be put off by the sarcastic tone used. She started spinning on the wheel where she had left the wool last time. Her spinning became very fine, and when finished, her Ladyship had to admit that it was amazingly well done.

Barbara proceeded to wind two bobbins of the spun wool together.

"Why are you doing that?" asked Elizabeth.

"One thread would easily break," answered Barbara, "so we must have two or more. It is called two or three ply. We knit the stockings with two ply and reinforce the heels and toes with three ply."

"Now let me see you knitting," ordered Elizabeth, still sceptical.

Thomas, who had sat silently watching the performance, asked Barbara what it was that she was strapping to her waist, with a leather belt.

"It is a knitting belt, Sir," she informed him. "Needles for knitting are inserted into one of the holes in the side of the belt, and it helps to keep the knitting even."

Thomas took the proffered leather sheath and examined it. "It is well made," he said.

Producing three long needles, (or wires as they are called in Shetland) Barbara began another stocking. She was in her element. Knowing the diamond pattern by heart, it did not take her long to knit a good piece. She knitted extremely fast.

Lady Busta sat, mouth open, staring unbelievingly at the speed at which the girl was knitting.

"I am sorry if I doubted your ability, Barbara, you certainly seem to have found your vocation," said Lady Busta.

"Yes," added Thomas, "you are quite an accomplished young lady – thanks to Martha and her skill in teaching you."

"Who do you sell your articles to?" asked her Ladyship.

"Martha sells them for me, Ma'am, they usually go to a shop in Lerwick."

"That will do for now Martha," said the lady, dismissing the knitters.

Once the door closed on the retreating figures and their goods, her Ladyship turned to Thomas;

"The audacity of the girl," she exclaimed, "earning money behind my back, and never a 'thank you' for all I have done for her."

"How much does she earn from you then," asked Thomas.

"Her keep," was the reply.

"But the girl needs something to set her up if she is going to marry in time," defended Thomas.

"Not if I can help it," shouted his wife as she left the room.

As Barbara expected, next day at breakfast time, Elizabeth accused her of cheating by making money and not telling her.

"In future," shouted Elizabeth, "you will give ME the 35/- you earn from your stockings. You have lived here free, but now you are earning you will pay for your keep like anyone else."

"But Ma'am," protested Barbara, "I do not keep the money. It is all sent to my mother, she is not able to earn for herself."

"I don't believe a word of that," accused Elizabeth.

"I can show you a letter from my mother," protested the girl, running from the room. A few moments later she reappeared with a letter from Mrs Pitcairn thanking Barbara for the amount of money she had sent so regularly, 35/-. It was a great help in keeping the household together. If it had not been for the regular payments coming in, she would have been out of the house long ago.

Barbara had handed the letter to Thomas to read, and as he looked at it, he felt ashamed to think that his wife could so wantonly accuse this innocent girl who had been unselfishly helping her mother.

"In future," said Thomas, "you will send half the money to your mother, and give Lady Busta, the rest."

Handing her her letter, Thomas nodded towards the door and the girl went out.

Martha was waiting outside for her. "Whatever happened?" she questioned Barbara.

Sobbing quietly, Barbara told Martha what the Giffords had said. Together they told cook who was very upset, but said they would think of something else for Barbara to do to get the extra money for her mother.

James came into the kitchen in a despondent mood. "Lowrie is leaving the stables tomorrow to join his father at the fishing," he told cook and Martha, "have you anyone in mind who would help instead?"

Martha shook her head. "Most of the youngsters have joined the fleet now," she said.

Cook smiled.

"Maybe I could help you there," she told James. She told him the story about the stockings and Barbara not being able to send the money to her mother.

"You know how fond Barbara is of the ponies, could she help you?"

"We could always ask her," said Martha.

At that moment the door opened and in walked Barbara.

"What has happened?" she queried, "you are all so quiet. Have you been talking about me?" she laughed.

"Yes, we have," confessed cook. "We were all trying to think of how you could make some extra money to send home."

Tears sprang to Barbara's eyes, she was touched by the concern of her friends.

"Oh, you must not worry," she assured them, "I shall think of something."

"Lowrie has left to work with his father," cook told her, "and we were just wondering if..."

"You thought I would like to take his place?" asked the girl, "But James, would you let me help? I do love the ponies so much."

At dinner that night, Barbara broached the subject of the stables.

"What? work in the stables, girl?" exploded Lady Busta, "whatever next?"

"Elizabeth," interrupted Thomas, "you criticise the girl for not paying for her keep, and now that she is, she cannot afford to help her mother. What does it matter to you how she makes some extra money? I admire her for being so resourceful. It was you who adopted her in the first place, remember?"

"But the stables!" she objected again.

"Let her give it a try at least," said Thomas kindly.

Barbara soon settled in at work at the stables. She especially loved exercising Elizabeth's pony, when James took Jasper out. She groomed and fed the ponies kept for the fishermen, and they soon came to recognise her as their friend.

It was heavy work at the stables, especially in the winter months when the ponies were fed by hand. Many of the wild ones out on the hills died, as a result of little grass and no shelter.

Chapter 11

JOHN INTERVENES

Elizabeth was always glad when John came home. He had been on a visit to Hamburg. He liked the foreign cities with their busy commerce, but it was good to return to the peace at home. The whole place seemed to be so uncluttered, the hills spacious and the air clean.

Barbara was missing from breakfast. Just as John asked what had happened to her the door opened and there stood Barbara, a bit dishevelled!

"Sorry," she apologised, "I shall not be eating breakfast this morning, Ma'am, I have been with Princess all night, as she is foaling. I hope the foal will be born soon."

"How dare you come barging in here, in that state, while we are eating, leave the room," bellowed her Ladyship.

Elizabeth was very angry that Barbara had come in with this announcement in front of John who wanted to know what she was doing at the stable.

"Come to my room after the meal and I will tell you," said Thomas, "I do not wish to speak of it at the meal-time."

Sitting across the fireplace from John, in the office, Thomas related to him the incident of the hosiery and how Barbara was trying to make some extra money to send to her mother. His wife had insisted on keeping half of what the girl earned for herself towards her keep.

John was furious.

"She was brought here as one of the family," he exploded, "how can Mother do this to her? It is preposterous, I shall find some other job for Barbara."

John went immediately to the stables where he found James and Barbara in the last stages of helping the young mare to foal. At last! A lovely little piebald foal appeared. The long night's vigil was over.

"Come, Barbara, you need a good rest," said John piloting the tired girl towards the house.

"But Princess needs attention," protested Barbara.

"James will see to her," John assured her.

Turning to James he said, "Barbara will not be coming to work at the stables again. I will see to it that someone else is sent."

Reaching the back door, John and Barbara removed their boots, and, passing through the kitchen John told Martha to take Barbara upstairs as she was exhausted. Cook was to take something hot up later.

At the foot of the stairs Barbara collapsed. Martha rushed to the kitchen to get a drink of water. John carried the poor girl up to her bedroom where she soon regained consciousness.

Casting his eye around the room, John was appalled to think that the rest of the family lived in luxury, while Barbara, supposed to be one of them, lived in a little attic room, barely furnished.

"Are you feeling better now?" Martha asked her, "I shall bring some breakfast up for you."

"You had no business to be working at the stables," reprimanded John "but I know why you did it. From now on you shall help Mother with the embroidery of the chair covers – that is a job more suited to a young lady like you. You will not pay for your keep if you sew for her."

Bending down, he gave her a light kiss on the cheek and felt surprised at the thrill he experienced. So different from kissing Jane Henderson, who his mother insisted they visit, at times. She lived in Bressay and was a most forward woman. A bit like his mother, he mused!

Barbara slept for hours and felt rested when she wakened. She was disappointed not to be allowed to go to the stables again, but realised it was not the job for her.

Martha came up with a hot drink and told Barbara to dress ready for helping Lady Busta with her embroidery.

It amazed Barbara how good it felt to be free to take a meal at leisure and sit to work the rest of the day.

One afternoon John asked Barbara to come a ride with him to Brae as he was going on business.

"I would rather go to Roe Sound," she answered. "Your mother might see us together as she always looks out of the window for the Master coming home."

When John had finished his work at Brae, he set off for Roe Sound and, there, in a sheltered spot, was Barbara. She was surprised to see John, who came and sat down beside her.

"I come here many times on my own," she told him, "I love the peace and quiet. I often dream of the life that could have been mine if only my father had not died. It has been so hard for mother, but now I am able to help her a little, I feel better."

"I am sorry my mother treats you as she does," John said.

It was warm in the afternoon sun and Barbara relaxing, lay back on the heathery hillside, her hair falling round her. John, lying beside her, ran his fingers through her hair, then kissed her cheek.

Barbara surprised, jumped up saying, "Let's get back, I have to dress for dinner."

"There is no hurry," chided John.

Mounting her pony, Barbara arrived back at the stables where she left the pony to the new groom to attend to.

Not for anything would she let John know what that kiss had meant to her. She had dreamed of it so often. She loved John, but he must not know.

Chapter 12

BARBARA's MISFORTUNES

It was nearing time for Beth to leave her employment at Busta House. In a way, she was happy, looking forward to her marriage to Malcolm, but at the same time, she would miss life at the big house and all the luxuries she had enjoyed when working there. Lady Busta had been pretty cruel at times and yet...

"Beth, come here at once," Lady Busta's voice broke into her thoughts. "I wish you to show Barbara how to do my hair. I have not got another girl to help me yet so may need to use Barbara's skills till I get one."

Actually her Ladyship had no intention of employing another girl in Beth's place. It was much cheaper to get Barbara to do the work and pay her a mere pittance after her food and lodgings had been deducted!

The next day Beth collected all her little belongings in her kist (wooden box). She knocked on the sitting-room door to announce her departure.

"Come in," Lady Busta shouted, "so you are just leaving. I trust you and Malcolm will have a happy life together. You have been a great help to me and my husband and I would like to give you a present on the occasion of your wedding."

Handing Beth a parcel, she continued, "You do not need to open it now, it is something I remembered you admired when you first came here. My small mirror!"

Tears welled up in Beth's eyes as she whispered, "Thank you Ma'am. I have enjoyed working for you, and I trust you will get someone else to help you soon."

"No doubt I shall," said Lady Busta near to tears herself. "Now go, Malcolm will be waiting for you."

As Beth quietly shut the door, Lady Busta took out her tiny lace handkerchief and dabbed her eyes. Beth was one in a million. But life had to go on. She rang the bell, and when Martha appeared, said "I am now employing Barbara Pitcairn to do for me the work that Beth has done. I shall expect her to have the same efficiency and promptness at all times. Please tell her to come here now."

"Yes, Ma'am," said a very surprised Martha.

A timid knock on the door was answered by Lady Busta shouting to Barbara to come in.

"Beth has just left," she told the girl, "and since it has been impossible for me to get another maid, I am employing you instead. She has shown you the ropes, so now it is up to you to do as I tell you. You will call me Ma'am when I speak to you."

"But, but, Ma'am," started Barbara in a hurt tone, "I thought I was to be treated as one of the family and not a servant!"

"Be quiet girl, and stop snivelling," shouted her ladyship, "I have given you a roof over your head. You should be grateful for that. Yet you stand there and defy me. How dare you. Come with me at once to my dressing room and do my hair for tonight."

"Yes Ma'am," said Barbara obediently.

When she had finished the hair-do, Barbara helped Lady Busta into her evening gown. "Hurry up girl and do up all the buttons, you will never be as efficient as Beth but as you are in my employment now, you will learn to do things my way, and in my time. Go now." A knock came to the door and John entered.

"What do you want?" asked Elizabeth irritably. She had not missed the love glance in John's eyes as he passed Barbara leaving the room.

"I heard you telling Barbara that you were employing her instead of Beth," stated John.

"Yes," snapped Lady Busta, "but what has that got to do with you?"

"That is impossible Mother. The girl is to be treated as one of the family, not, as she said, a 'Servant'! I love the girl, and," but he got no further.

"You what?" shrieked Lady Busta, nearly bursting a blood vessel.

"I will marry Barbara Pitcairn in spite of the world," stated John stoutly and left the room.

Lady Busta kept a keen eye open for any sign of John and Barbara speaking with each other, but she need not have bothered. Being denied the privilege of speaking openly, they continued to meet in secret.

Lady Busta had many personal friends. She enjoyed entertaining them in the garden on a fine day.

At one of these parties an unsuspecting visitor admired Barbara and innocently remarked;

"She would make John a fine wife!" To which Lady Busta declared, "I would rather see my son John dead at my feet than wedded to Barbara Pitcairn."

......

Once the household had gone to bed, Barbara tip-toed downstairs and let herself out of a small window then crept down the side of the garden wall to the little pier where John sat waiting in the boat. Casting off the rope, Barbara jumped into the boat and John silently rowed out of the harbour. Keeping under cover of the cliffs, the boat glided along to a small inlet where John beached her. Helping Barbara on to the sand, they both ran up the beach to a favourite spot, flinging themselves down on the grass to enjoy each other's company for a few hours. Lying in each other's arms, all else was forgotten – Hamburg, Lady Busta, orders.

"Barbara Pitcairn, I love you," whispered John, "and I am going to marry you."

Barbara was stunned.

"But John," she began, "we could never do that, your parents would never give consent."

"My parents need never know about it," said John as he put an arm around her, "we shall get Rev John Fisken to marry us in secret!"

As Barbara was getting into the boat her foot slipped and she fell, hitting the side of her cheek on the boat. She cried out in pain. John gathered her up in his arms and held her tight.

"I wouldn't have wanted this to happen to you, my love, for all the world, you are so lovely. I can't bear anything to hurt you."

John was very upset. He gave Barbara his handkerchief to hold on the cut, then settled her in the boat and rowed back to the harbour. He carried her up to the little gate in the wall and gave her a last kiss as he set her down.

"We shall not be able to meet much longer like this," observed John, "the moon is starting to make the evenings lighter. We shall have to go a walk instead. See you at breakfast. Be careful," he whispered giving her a hug.

Next morning at breakfast, as all were seated, Lady Busta looked across at Barbara, horrified.

"Good gracious child, what have you done with your face?" she said, drawing everyone's attention to it.

"I tripped coming in last night." Barbara told her.

"Go to Martha immediately and get her to put something on it, it looks terrible," said Lady Busta.

"Mother," interrupted John, "it was not Barbara's fault if she fell. Her face looks really sore. Come, Barbara, I will take you to Martha."

"Sit down, John," bellowed her Ladyship, "the girl is quite capable of going herself."

Martha was appalled at the state of Barbara's face.

"Sit there just now, dear, till I take the breakfast to the dining-room. I'll get you a hot cup of tea in a minute."

Martha, missing Beth very much, had instantly accepted Barbara. She seemed to fit into any situation, but she also felt sorry for her by the way she had been belittled in the household.

Back in the kitchen, Martha put salve on the wound and said, "This will heal quicker if left free to the air. How did it happen?"

"I was coming home when I tripped and caught my cheek on something sharp," was the reply.

Barbara was excused attending lessons with the tutor, but instead had to sit by Lady Busta and unpick a number of rows of embroidery which her ladyship had had the misfortune to sew incorrectly.

Poor Barbara was in a state of nervousness in case she was asked about the details of the accident. Little did she anticipate how that was nearly found out.

As Barbara got up from the stool she usually sat on, Lady Busta said in a peculiar voice, "And what, may I ask is Master John's handkerchief doing in YOUR pocket, girl?"

Barbara's face went red. "Ma'am, as I came home yesterday, I fell."

"Yes, yes," interrupted that impatient woman, "but how did the handkerchief get there? Let me see, it's, covered in blood," she exclaimed.

"Yes Ma'am, Master John was passing at the time I fell, he gave me this to dab my face," Barbara started to cry.

At that moment the door opened.

"What is all the fuss about, Mother?"

"You may well ask, son. This girl, I find, has one of YOUR handkerchiefs in HER pocket. Can you explain?" she asked.

"Quite easily, Mother, she was in front of me, when she fell. When I saw she had hurt her face and that it was bleeding, I gave her my handkerchief."

"I see," said Lady Busta, then turning to Barbara, "if you have finished unpicking my embroidery, give it to me, and leave the room."

"How can you be so hard on her, Mother. You have not got Beth now, and I doubt if you would ever get anyone like Barbara to help you," warned John.

"I was not asking for your opinion, John, and when I want it I will make it clear to you. You can go now."

Lady Busta sat back in her chair. "I suppose I was a bit hard on the girl but I have a suspicious mind. As she is under my roof as a protègè, I can treat her as I please," and with that, she shut her eyes for her morning nap.

Meanwhile John went to the kitchen to see Barbara, who was feeling better, but Martha was very upset still.

Chapter 13

JANE HENDERSON

It was a lovely day so Lady Busta ordered afternoon tea to be served on the upper lawn.

"Christina, your dancing master will be here in a moment. Andrina, will you see that William and Hay are ready for him when he comes, he hates to be kept waiting. I see Amy coming and here is Jack," she observed.

John Fisken stayed at Busta House, but had been across the voe in the boat and was returning. John went to meet him. They were good friends.

"Tell me when you are ready to leave after the lessons today," said John, "I want to speak to you on a private matter."

"Yes, sure," said John Fisken, "I'll be glad to."

John Fisken and John settled down to drink tea.

"Barbara is excused lessons today," Lady Busta told them, "she apparently fell yesterday and hurt her face. It is nothing, but she can join you tomorrow."

John Fisken was quite upset at not having Barbara at the class that day. She was as bright as any of the Gifford family, and he thought she was very beautiful too. He would wait his time, and at a convenient moment ask Lady Busta if he could take Barbara out walking. He was sure she was the right one for him.

John Fisken was in for a shock! As he and John walked slowly down the Willow Walk and out of the gates at the foot of the garden, John asked John Fisken if he would marry him and Barbara Pitcairn.

"John Gifford, you don't really mean to tell me you are wanting me to secretly marry you and Barbara?" asked the young man incredulously. "It can't be done." John Fisken had gone ashen-white.

"Why not?" enquired John in an amused tone, "I will never get permission from my parents, and I love her. Besides I am thirty years old and should be married with a family of my own. Will you agree to do it then?"

"I suppose so," said John Fisken grudgingly, seeing his opportunity of wooing Barbara fast fading away.

"Good," smiled John. "I'll work something out and let you know."

Lady Busta had hardly slept for weeks. John had told her he was going to marry Barbara Pitcairn, but Lady Busta was determined that the marriage would never take place. She was not going to be replaced by that woman, or any other. If Thomas Gifford died, the new laird's wife would become head of the household at Busta House, and while Elizabeth remained there, she, and only she, would be mistress.

Several times Elizabeth had invited Mr and Mrs Henderson of Garth, in Bressay for a weekend. If John became engaged to their daughter, it would let Barbara Pitcairn know for certain that she would not be the future Mrs Gifford.

John had recently been invited to Jane's birthday party so Lady Busta decided to buy a pair of Barbara's lace hose for her present. It was far too expensive but what does one give to a girl who seems to have everything.

John, unknown to his mother, had committed his life to Barbara and had no intention of getting involved with Miss Henderson.

Fortunately, in Lerwick on the day of the party, John met a colleague from his college days. Peter Magnusson, a Shetlander, was a doctor and was back in the islands in connection with smallpox vaccinations.

John had an idea. He would take Peter to the party and introduce him to Miss Henderson, hoping he would find her more intriguing than he did!

"We shall meet here at the pier," John told Peter, "about 8.30pm. See you then".

Arriving on Bressay, John and Peter made their way to Garth House. Mr and Mrs Henderson welcomed them. Their daughter made such a fuss at seeing John again, but once introduced to Dr Peter, John was ignored!

During the meal, Mrs Henderson had sat John next to her daughter, maybe hoping like Lady Busta, to hear the engagement announcement that evening.

The meal had been extravagantly provided and the wine flowed freely.

Miss Henderson was handed her presents at the table and she received many lovely gifts. John gave her his present, also that of his mother's. The girl opened the parcel and found the lace hose. Her mother was amazed at the expensive, unique present. Not many had cost so much.

Miss Henderson, looking at the stockings said in a condescending voice, "I never wear Shetland wool next to my skin, it is too coarse!" She let them drop to the floor.

One of the other ladies present was appalled. "My goodness," she said, "and they are so beautifully knitted. Quite a work of art."

John was livid, but tried not to show it. He found himself comparing this woman to Barbara. Miss Henderson's face was plastered with white powder and her lips covered with red paint. Barbara's cheeks were fresh and soft as a peach when he kissed them, and her lips were perfect.

Thinking of Barbara, made him look to where the present lay on the floor, being kicked around by peoples' feet as they passed by.

Putting a hand on the back of Jane's chair, he spoke softly in her ear. "We'll never marry."

John was glad he had delivered his message. The recipient seemed rather intoxicated, so he had no idea whether she had heard it or not.

John scooped the parcel up from the floor, and putting it in his pocket, left the room. He thought of all the work dear Barbara had put into making the gift. It was not going to be thrown away like that.

Entering a boat, John suddenly thought of Peter. Oh, well he could find his own way back to the town if he could tear himself away from 'her'.

When John arrived back at Busta House next day, his mother asked excitedly how the party had gone. She was very upset when John told her that he had left the house-party in full swing. He had introduced a friend of his to Miss Henderson and she seemed enchanted by him.

His mother, thinking John was upset by the fact that he had been ignored, assured him not to worry, they would invite the Hendersons for another weekend soon.

"I would rather you left her out of my life, Mother," he said with anger as he thought of the gift in his pocket and the state he had left Miss Henderson in.

Chapter 14

COUSIN WILLIAM

Some days the Laird and his wife would be so busy, they only had a chance to review the happenings of the day, exchange news, or family affairs, when they retired to the drawing-room after dinner.

"By the way, Betty," began Thomas, "I had a letter today from our cousin Mistress Watt in Edinburgh, asking if her son William could come and stay with us for a few weeks. It seems he has been suffering from crewels in the hand. He is a delicate lad and maybe a holiday at Busta would put a bit of colour in his cheeks. What do you say to it, my dear?"

"Yes, I expect he could come," said her Ladyship reluctantly, "he is such a spoilt boy and always wants his own way. I suppose, being an only child, he has everything he wants but health."

Heaving a sigh of relief, Thomas asked, "When I write Mistress Watt then, can I tell her William can come? I am only having the boy because I feel sorry for him."

"No doubt," sulked Elizabeth, thinking about their bank balance.

It was a few weeks before William arrived. He certainly looked a frail boy. After his long journey in the boat from Leith, then open boat to Busta, Elizabeth saw that he was put to bed immediately, where he slept a full day. Although Elizabeth did not have much sympathy with people who were ill, she called the family doctor from Lunnasting to come and have a look at the boy, especially his hand. The Doctor prescribed a medicine and said he would be in the district in a week's time so would look along again then.

Hay was given the job of keeping William occupied. He refused to go to lessons with the other children. Hay met him in the hallway afterwards and asked him if he would like to come for a ride on his pony, Rowan.

"No thanks," said William sullenly, "I do not like horses, one cannot trust them."

"Rowan is all right," protested Hay, "she is only a Shetland pony and is very quiet. Come on William, you'll love her."

"I won't go near a horse," said William, stamping his foot.

"All right then, what about playing ball in the field?" asked Hay.

"No thank you," William replied, "I have a bad hand."

"But we would only be kicking it around," laughed Hay. "Let us go a walk then."

"No thank you," replied William stolidly again.

"Well what do you play with your friends in Leith then?" asked a puzzled Hay!

"I do not have any friends in Leith." replied William.

"Not much wonder," said Hay going out of the door.

William started to cry, and Lady Busta coming down the stairs asked what was the matter.

"It is Hay, he is very cruel to me," sobbed the boy.

"Excuse me Ma'am," interrupted Martha, who had been dusting the stairs and hallway and heard the conversation, "Master Hay was very polite and offered to take your guest on his pony or for a walk or play ball, but he," indicating William, "would not go."

"I see," said her Ladyship, "in that case, you will come upstairs and read to me while I do my embroidery. I presume you can read."

"Yes Ma'am," said William relieved he did not have to be with Hay.

William's hand was no better when the doctor called the next week, so he suggested he took the boy back to Lunnasting with him. William was glad of the idea as he hated Hay who teased him sometimes. Hay could not understand the boy he had offered to help.

So it was that William arrived at Lunna.

......

Thomas Gifford looked forward each day to the time when he and James spent discussing the affairs of the Estate and supplies for the many boats arriving for the fishing.

"Did you manage to get word to the crofters that we will need all the milk, cheese, eggs, butter, oil and meat they can supply? I believe another fifty boats are arriving from Holland and coming here after they have reported to the Customs at Lerwick. Did you engage another two men to help out at the Booth. There are four already, but we also need the extra men. As the season develops we may need more."

"Yes, sir," James replied, "I got two lads from Roe. They will go home each night so will not require accommodation."

"Good for you James," Thomas said thankfully, "I can always rely on you. Now about the Orkney boats, they will be delivering their goods soon, we usually pay them by cash. As the Dutch and Germans pay us well, we will have enough to pay the Orcadians back".

"We will need to order more lines, sir," added James, who had made a list of requirements from the Booth. "This is the list we need; salted fish, butter, oil, a few herrings, coarse hose. I also made out a list of things we need to be brought back from Hamburg: if Master John is there now could we get word to him to collect it?

"24 Barrels Gr lines and 8 Do Tomlines

"30 Matts Hollands roll tobacco

"20 Barrels 100 Anker Corn Spirals

"20 Hogsheads best French brandy

"10,000 ling hooks, 12,000 Haddock Dos

"8 Barrels tar wrack pipe styves Barrel hopes

"I trust you will not think me forward sir, but when we sent word to the crofters for those food supplies I also mentioned more hose, we are always in need of the coarse hose for the Dutchmen. The finer stockings are sold at the ports back home, along with hats and gloves."

"Not at all James, you do well and I leave it to your judgement. I shall write Anthony Simpson again in Hamburgh. He is always quibbling over the orders I give him and says we do not send enough articles in return for all we expect him to do. The audacity of the man! I expect him to ransom my ship, pay their insurance, and supply the boats with necessities for their voyages. He credits my bills, and sends supplies here for the fishing. I always ask for some hard cash. I don't think we are unreasonable, do you?"

"Just as you say sir," replied James raising an eyebrow.

Thomas Gifford frowned as he studied the business books. Things were not going as well as he would have liked. John was in Germany at the time so he felt he must write to him and see if he could help. The date on his letter was 29th July, 1744. The weather being bad, boats full of cod and herring were delayed ten days. 'I am sunk in debt at Hamburg. We need the cash to pay for a great deal of purchases here',

John was not successful in helping his father, in fact, while in Hamburg he had spent more than he had intended.

There were many shops in the town, of different kinds, in the little narrow streets. As John passed one of the jewellers, he stopped and looked in the window. Now was his chance to buy a ring for Barbara. He chose a gold one and had their initials engraved inside.

Arriving back at the Seaman's House John got a shock as he read his father's letter.

He reported back to the captain when loading of the ship began again with the usual items such as salt, lines, hooks and other things for the fishing.

Soon they headed for home.

"While I am writing Simpson," reported Thomas Gifford, "I shall forward a letter to John as well. He is in Hamburg presently. I shall tell them I leave all my business in Hamburg entirely to them and they can do what they judge best. It is impossible for me to form any right notion thereof in these confused uncertain times."

James nodded. John and Farquhar would no doubt think this an honour to be in charge of Gifford's affairs abroad, but in reality Gifford was handing over the sinking ship.

"By the way, James, what are we charging for a barrel of herring?" he asked.

"We charge 5/- a barrel, sir," answered James, "3 pence for a ling, and 1 pence for a cod. That covers the cost of labour and pilotage etc.,"

"Not enough, not enough," grumbled Gifford.

"If we put the prices up, sir, they just will not buy and we will be worse off," James pointed out.

Chapter 15

SECRET WEDDING

Unfortunately, Robert, whom John would have liked for his 'best man' at the wedding, was away on business at the time. Robbie was only eighteen when he was put on board a ship going to Oporto, Portugal. Captain Francis Bull was a hard man and Robbie had many unpleasant tasks to perform.

John asked William and Hay to be witnesses instead.

By rights, John Gifford should have faced his parents and married Barbara in the legal manner. As it was, things were done in such an underhand way that John Fisken even omitted the proclamation of the Banns. He was a man of indifferent character and often drank too much. He had no time for Lady Busta as he had often witnessed her poor treatment of Barbara, who was more like a servant than a guest in the house.

John Fisken, William and Hay were sworn to secrecy about the wedding. John contacted the butler in Whalsay to find out if Lady Symbister and her husband were likely to be away from the house soon, as he was wanting to have a wedding at the Laird's house. Lamb, the butler, sent word that Lady Symbister and her husband would be visiting in the Dunrossness area shortly.

The date fixed was the 8th December, and Symbister House would be looked after by a skeleton staff. Lamb was willing to make a feast for the wedding when the party arrived.

John told his mother that he thought it would be a good time to take William and Hay to see their friends in Whalsay for a few days holiday, they had been invited often.

"Yes," said Lady Busta. "I suppose you could go now. The weather is not too good. It is not a busy time of year so your father will not miss you so much as in the summer months."

John smiled. Now he had to think of some excuse to get Barbara away too, but Lady Busta had already arranged for Barbara and Alice to visit their mother in Lerwick as they had not seen her since coming to Busta.

It was arranged that James would take the party, including Barbara and Alice, in the boat to Olnafirth, where John's party would travel on ponies to Laxo Voe, catching the ferry to Symbister while Barbara and Alice were to ride to Catfirth and catch a ferry to Lerwick.

All was working out perfectly right under Lady Busta's nose yet she was not aware of anything untoward.

The weather, though bitterly cold, was dry and sunny. After packing her prettiest frock and shoes, Barbara took her little cloth bag to the boat and waited for the boys to come.

Beth arrived to help Lady Busta while Barbara was away.

William and Hay were very excited about the prospect of a holiday. It was years since they had been in Whalsay. Hay was a baby then. It was quite an adventure now – especially being on a secret mission!

When James left the party at Olnafirth, he had an uneasy feeling – a premonition that all was not well. However, he turned the boat and rowed for Busta again.

John ran over to where Barbara and Alice were mounting their ponies and led them to where the party was waiting to go to Laxo Voe.

Once on the Whalsay ferry boat, John heaved a sigh of relief. He sat back in the boat and shut his eyes. He could not believe that everything had gone so smoothly.

"I just hope Lamb has a good feed ready for us when we arrive, I'm starving" said Hay.

"Trust you to think of food," laughed William settling back in his seat.

"I hope they have a good supply of wine," said John Fiskin, grimacing to himself.

Barbara sat in silence, thinking her own thoughts. If only her father had lived, they would have been well-off like the Giffords. As young girls, she and Elise would draw their wedding frocks, veils, shoes and bouquets – they were wonderful! but it was no use dreaming about that now. She would be married to John Gifford tomorrow and be the future 'Mrs Gifford of Busta.' A smile stole across her pretty face.

"Tell us the joke," laughed William. Barbara said nothing. Her thoughts had been no joke.

Each one alighted from the boat at Whalsay and, after paying 8/- for each passenger, John helped Barbara ashore.

"Are you all right?" he queried, as Barbara seemed so quiet.

"Yes, thanks John, I am just a bit afraid of the water," she replied.

Lamb was waiting their arrival at the pier with the gig.

Arriving at Symbister House, two servant girls showed the party to their rooms. They were all grateful for their beds that night. It had been a long, tiring journey with the added excitement of the trip.

The 8th day of December, 1747, turned out to be perfect. Sun shining, a little frost, but a lovely day.

Barbara was up early. After breakfast she dressed in her pretty turquoise, taffeta frock, which was crinoline style. Her hair was in ringlets, caught up with two small turquoise clasps – a present from John which he had brought from Hamburg. She had never worn them at Busta House in case Lady Busta asked from whom she had received them. Her dainty shoes matched her frock and she carried a small bouquet of flowers she found on a table.

The wedding ceremony was being held in the drawing-room at 10 am. A servant knocked on Barbara's door to tell her that everyone was in the room waiting for her to arrive.

Barbara and Alice followed the girl downstairs and, as they entered the room John gasped, he had never seen Barbara looking so beautiful.

He came forward, and taking her hand, led her to the table, where the Rev John Fisken stood ready to take them through the ceremony.

William and Hay stood one each side of the bridal couple and smiled at them as they took their place.

The Rev John Fisken looked grave as he always did at funerals and weddings. Today, he seemed almost morose. He felt it should have been he who was marrying this beautiful girl, and in a proper church wedding, not a secret affair like this. He had chided John once or twice about it and also asked where the couple would live once they were married. John told him to mind his own business or he would lose his job at Busta House. John Fisken could not afford to do that, so he suffered in silence.

The crowning injustice was having to join John and Barbara in matrimony. He jerked his head upright as John Gifford gave a little cough. It was no use day-dreaming.

"Shall we bow our heads in prayer," he said to hide his confusion. "We shall now read a couple of passages from the Bible. Now please repeat the marriage vows after me."

After this part of the ceremony was over, William produced a gold ring which John placed on Barbara's finger.

"I now pronounce you man and wife," said John Fisken in a strained voice.

John Gifford kissed his wife, she was legally his, at last.

William and Hay were proud to have Barbara as their sister-in-law.

Lamb announced that the wedding meal was ready, and the company walked into the dining-room, after the bridal pair, where a feast awaited them – and what a spread! There was also an abundance of the best wine from Lady Symbister's vast store of wine in the cellar.

The bride and groom were toasted, then all sat down to eat and drink.

As man and wife, John and Barbara enjoyed the lovely room they could happily share together. Barbara wished it could be like this for ever.

Next day was spent, for some, getting over sore heads. John and Barbara walked over the island, taking a picnic with them. They found a sheltered cove where they sat and enjoyed each other's company. They returned to the house in time for dinner.

William and Hay had had a great day at the shore with Lamb, who pointed out seals and porpoise playing. Alice remained at the house, fascinated by the pictures and portraits in the rooms.

It was soon time to return to Busta House. Barbara was quite upset. "John, when will we be able to be on our own, if at all?" she queried.

"Don't worry," he replied trying to placate her, "we'll work something out. By the way, take off the ring. Mother must never see you wearing it."

"But John, we are married now," cried Barbara.

"Do as I tell you Barbara, don't be awkward, you know what Mother is like."

Before returning to Busta, Barbara took a piece of wool on which she strung the ring, tying it round her neck.

"I shall wear it always," she said to herself, "in spite of Lady Busta."

The party was reluctant to leave the safety of Symbister House, but as 'all good things come to an end', they had to return.

The boat had not arrived yet to take them back to Laxo Voe so John suggested to Barbara that they visit the Hanseatic Booth. John, speaking fluent German, was able to converse with the owner and talked about the fishing.

Seeing a roll of lovely black lace, Barbara nudged John's elbow.

"Is that for sale?" she asked.

"Yes, madam," said the German in good English, "would you desire a piece?"

"Do you think we could buy a length," Barbara asked. "It is so beautiful".

"Certainly," said John.

Wrapping the lace up carefully, the man handed it to Barbara, and John paid for it.

"Look at that gorgeous fur," said Barbara, "how I would love to wear something like that."

"You shall, one day," said John, "when we get settled on our own. I would love to buy it for you now."

"That one came from Russia," said the owner of the booth. "We buy furs from them and exchange our goods. That is a really valuable one."

"I promise you, Barbara," said John putting an arm round her as they left the booth, "I shall buy one like that for you, and many more beautiful things".

Lamb saw them to the boat, then returned to the house to tidy up after the party had gone.

It was decided on reaching Laxo Voe, that Barbara and her sister would go to Lerwick, while John and his brothers ride to Olnafirth and catch the ferry to Brae.

The girls enjoyed a couple of days with their mother, but never mentioned the wedding. How different it would have been, Barbara reflected, if she could have taken her mother into her confidence, but she dare not.

On John's return, his mother lost no time in asking how Lady Symbister was keeping.

"You'll never believe it Mother, but they had just left the day before for Sumburgh to stay with Mrs Bruce," said John, relieved to think of some excuse.

"But she never told ME she was going," accused Lady Busta.

"Mother, everyone does not tell you all that is going on," protested John.

"Father, we went into the Halseatic Booth before leaving Whalsay. I had an interesting conversation with the owner, then bought a piece of lovely lace we left with Lamb to give Lady Symbister as a 'thank you' for being at her house. I nearly bought Ba...." John stopped short, he remembered in the nick of time not to mention Barbara's name!

"Bought Barbara what?" yelled Lady Busta.

"A birthday present for you," he corrected, "of a fur, but I did not know if you would like to wear it or not. Would you?"

Lady Busta sat upright in her chair – smoothing her newly acquired tussau silk frock.

"Yes, I think I would John," she answered, "there are not any around here, now I come to think of it. I would be the first to appear in one. Just imagine, a Russian fur!"

......

James was sent to meet Barbara and her sister two days later.

"How did you enjoy Lerwick?" Lady Busta asked. "It is a long time since you were there."

"Yes," Barbara replied, "it was good to see Mother again. She was looking a lot better and sends her regards."

Thank goodness, she thought, she does not suspect anything.

Chapter 16

THE BOATING ACCIDENT

Five months after the wedding, on a lovely day in May, the Gifford sons, having nothing better to do, decided to visit their Uncle Andrew and cousins at Wethersta. They suggested that John, Barbara and Elise come too for the trip. James rowed them over the Voe, where they spent a very pleasant afternoon.

Next day at breakfast time, John said, "I heard that there are seals and otters around Hillswick. Come on boys, we'll take the guns and go shooting!"

"No, you can't," interrupted Barbara, "that is a cruel sport."

"That is not for you to decide, Barbara Pitcairn," Lady Busta scathingly remarked.

"How can you think to kill those lovely harmless creatures?" continued Barbara, "with their beautiful eyes, they are so helpless – John please," she pleaded.

"How dare you talk to Master John in such a manner girl, leave the room at once," bellowed Lady Busta.

Barbara, rising from the table, brushed a tear from her face.

For a moment John Gifford felt quite strange – he had upset the girl he loved, and was going to go against her wishes by heedlessly killing those lovely animals.

"Mother," interrupted Hay, "I also feel like Barbara, it is a cruel, wicked sport!"

"Get out of the room also," shouted his mother, who by this time was beside herself with rage.

Hay caught up with Barbara as she disconsolately climbed the stairs to her room.

"Oh, Hay, I hate to see animals killed for sport," she cried.

"So do I, Barbara, I shall do all I can to stop them going," he assured her.

71

John, Robbie and William began to prepare for the day's shooting. Cook made ready a large hamper with meat, chicken, home-made bread, also bottles of wine and fresh milk.

Lady Busta came to the door to see her sons away on their day trip.

"Where is Hay," she asked.

"He did not want to come," answered William. "He is not keen on the shooting".

"He will go," said her ladyship, "if I have to carry him on board myself. Not keen on shooting – indeed!"

"Hay!" she hollered, "come here at once."

Hay appeared, slowly descending the stairs.

"And where may you have been hiding?" she questioned, glaring at him. "Get your coat and boots and go with the others".

At this, she turned from the door and went to the sitting-room, where she could watch the party from her upstairs window.

There was Hay at the rear of the procession, looking very dejected. Elizabeth began to have misgivings about forcing the boy to go with the others, after all, he was only fifteen. Maybe she should call him back. She had never seen a seal killed and the thought of shooting one of these helpless animals began to haunt her.

Elizabeth knocked on the window several times until her hand hurt, then turning away, sat in her armchair and picked up her embroidery. After a moment or two, she rang the bell.

"Fetch me a cup of strong tea," she ordered Barbara, then sat back in her chair trying to forget the recent episode.

As the rowing boat left the pier, William was anxious about Hay who was quite upset. He had led a sheltered life, being the youngest son, the older brothers and sisters had rather spoilt him. He was a kind-hearted, gentle boy who could not bear to see anything hurt.

Passing Muckle Roe (the big red island), the sun shone on the beautiful red stone of the cliffs. They passed three small islands, Linga, Papa Little (small island of the Priest), and Vementry, a rich green. Once through Swarbacks Minn, the boat was in the Atlantic Ocean.

Putting up the sail, the boat gathered speed before the wind, which gave James a chance to 'rest on the oars'.

Seven miles were soon covered, passing high cliffs filled with sea-birds, nesting.

Robert was the first to see some seals lying up on the rocks near the bay at Hillswick.

"Please Robert," pleaded Hay, "don't shoot them."

But Robert lifted his gun and aimed at the largest one and it cried out in pain as the shot went into its side. Rolling off the stone, it disappeared into the dark water, leaving a red stain. The other seals had already dived into the sea.

Hay was beside himself with grief. He covered his head with a jacket and lay in the stern of the boat on a sack.

John was next to shoot, despite the pleadings from his wife, still ringing in his ears. He fired and killed another seal, also basking on the rocks. William could not resist taking a shot at one which swam near to the boat!

By this time, Hay was very sick, and kept asking to be taken home.

"I wish Mother had never interfered," said Robert querulously, "we could have had a great day without Hay."

"Let's have our hamper of food now," said William, hoping it might help Hay to forget the killings.

But the poor boy just cried and cried, and when the others realised that he was not going to be pacified, John told James to turn the boat and head for home.

As the boat entered the sound of Swarbacks Minn, James found the rowing very difficult. A seaman of many years he had never experienced a situation like this before. He rowed as hard as he could, but the boat would not move and seemed to be stuck in the same position.

Fear began to settle on the occupants of the boat and they felt cold with fright. John Fisken said they should pray, which they did. James tried rowing again, but nothing happened. The water was smooth, not a ripple on it. John Fisken, this time knelt down in the boat and, hands together, pleaded with God to let them be able to row home again.

James put the oars over the side to row, but oh! what was that? Three creatures like huge seals seemed to come from under the boat and swim away.

"It's all your faults," shouted poor Hay, who had by this time been as anxious as the rest that the boat would be all right. "It's just God punishing you for killing the seals."

The Rev John Fisken looked at the three older men and spoke to them, "Someone has sinned more than ordinary magnitude. He will have to obtain forgiveness before going to sea again."

......

Next week, William suggested visiting their Uncle Andrew again at Wethersta. They might as well enjoy the leisure days before the rush of the fishing season started again.

John tried to persuade Barbara, as they lay together in the little attic room, to come with him to Wethersta.

"I was very upset, John," said Barbara, "when you went shooting, and for her Ladyship forcing Hay to go too. The boy will never forget those awful scenes as long as he lives, also that terrible experience on the way home. Poor soul, he came to me to be comforted, he is a loveable boy and so kind to everyone. His mother did not even want to hear the details of the trip. She will never know how hurt he was. I shall try to help him all I can."

"Barbara, you help everyone. You have helped me, love, and I feel so ashamed to be living like this, when we should have our own home. I shall fix up something when I go to Wethersta tomorrow. I wish you would come too. I love you and want the best for you, but that will never be under this roof while Mother is alive.

"I better creep down to my own room again," he whispered, "in case she is prowling the corridors."

So saying, he took Barbara in his arms and kissed her passionately before leaving the room.

"Be sure to take your jacket tomorrow with the certificate in it. Don't leave it in the house whatever you do, your mother may find it," Barbara added. "I love you too. God bless."

John stole down to his own room to lie awake and think for hours. He would ask Uncle Andrew if he could rent him a house as he no longer could stay in Busta House.

He had to find somewhere he could take Barbara safely to before they could make their marriage known.

The weather was beautiful and Saturday, the 14th May, turned out mild and sunny.

John, Robert, William and John Fisken all discussed the forthcoming trip to Wethersta.

Thomas Gifford asked Hay if he was going too.

"No Father," Hay said emphatically, "I shall never go in a boat again. I got such a fright, last time. The seals were paying us back for killing their friends."

"Now, now, son," cautioned his father, "you must not blame them."

"No," intervened John Fisken loudly, "it is a worse sin than that, that has to be forgiven," he finished, looking across at John Gifford.

Barbara blushed.

When breakfast finished, John went in search of James.

"Good morning sir. What plans have you for today?" queried James.

"Well James, it is another lovely day, we might as well make the best of it. The lads and I are thinking to go across to Wethersta before lunch, so you can keep the day clear to row us over."

"Fine, sir, I shall see to it that I am clear by 12 noon," replied James.

As John strode off to the stables, he met Hay coming out with his pony Frisky.

"Where are you off to at this time of day?" he asked.

"I am going to Wethersta." Hay replied.

"What, on horseback? Are you not coming with us in the boat?" laughed John. His smile faded as he saw Hay's face go white.

"I'm sorry Hay about what happened yesterday," apologised John, "I had no idea you were so upset about the seals. I should have found a way of persuading Mother that you really did not wish to go."

Hay mounted Frisky, and rode away.

"Take care," John shouted after him.

Once on his pony, Hay left Busta and, keeping to the path, rode for the head of the voe. He had a 3 mile journey ahead of him but he loved riding and it helped to clear his mind.

He stopped at the pier at Brae to have a look at the Dutch boats which had arrived. The booths would be going up soon and Hay enjoyed accompanying his father or brothers there when they came to do business with the foreigners.

Hay mounted his pony again and rode past the small crofts with thatched cottages. Ponies and cows were tethered outside while hens, dogs and cats strayed around the doors. Often the children would come and speak to Hay and pat Frisky.

Hay settled to a steady trot and sang as he rode along. All of a sudden, Frisky reared up and whinnied. An otter, coming up from the beach, had crossed the road just in front of them. Hay patted Frisky's neck and told him to calm down. He was very thankful to know that this little otter was safe.

Arriving at Wethersta, his Uncle greeted Hay warmly.

They all loved Hay. "Come on, lad," said Uncle Andrew, "I'll take you to see our latest arrival in the stable. She was born this morning."

Hay was fascinated with the lovely little foal, a Shetland piebald.

"She is beautiful," he laughed, "what will you call her?"

"Could you help me with a name?" his uncle asked.

"She will be called 'Beauty of Wethersta'," answered Hay patting her. He gave a handful of hay to the mare, Sheila, who nuzzled his elbow. She loved Hay and had often taken him rides when he was younger.

"So this is where you are?" John said coming round the corner of the stables. "I might have guessed, among the animals!"

"Come and see 'Beauty of Wethersta'," Hay said excitedly, "Uncle let me name her. What do you think? Isn't that a good choice?"

"Wonderful," answered John patting Hay on the shoulder. "Now, run along and find the others. I have business to talk with Uncle Andrew."

"Well, John, what can I do for you?" asked his uncle, who was very fond of John.

"I am in need of a house of my own," began John. "All father's houses are occupied. I need a place to live and be independent. I believe one of your tenants left that house near the shore recently. Would it be possible to rent it from you for a while, until I get something more suitable?"

"Why, John, of course. I would be delighted to have you living near by," smiled Uncle Andrew.

Joining the others, John felt at ease. He could now bring Barbara over to Wethersta, away from his mother, and be able to announce that they were married. He could just imagine Barbara's delight.

The brothers spent a happy day at Wethersta, and, coming up to midnight, made ready to go home.

Hay announced, "I'll race you home," and ran out of the house to untie Frisky and start off before the others had a chance to reach the boat. However Frisky was not tied to his usual stake, so Hay went to the stables, but no pony there! Hay got quite worried. He went in search of James to ask if he had put the pony in a field.

"No," said James, "I have not touched him." Everyone was questioned but to no avail. No-one had seen Frisky.

"He maybe got loose and went home on his own for his supper," suggested John, "but never mind, it is getting late so you will have to come in the boat with us."

"No, I will not," screamed Hay, "I hate the boat. Maybe the seals will upturn the boat and we'll all be drowned."

"Don't talk nonsense," said Robbie, "I'll sit beside you. Look, William is already in the boat. Come." As he made a dive for Hay, Robbie just missed him.

"Come on now," said John in a peremptory voice, "get into the boat, at once". He caught hold of Hay, who by this time was kicking and screaming.

"Do as you are told," John commanded, lifting the boy on board.

"We'll all be drowned," shouted Hay, "we'll all be drowned."

"James, start rowing," shouted John, "and that way he will have to sit still."

"Yes, sir," said James putting the oars out. John Fisken was looking sullen. He had not yet come to terms with the secret marriage and wished he could pay John Gifford back in some way for treating Barbara as a servant in the house.

John put his hat and stick under the seat and prepared to enjoy the journey back to Busta Harbour.

It was a beautiful, moonlit evening – the water calm and not a ripple to be seen as the boat glided silently across the water of the voe from Wethersta.

It would not be long now till John could creep up the stairs and be with Barbara again.

Hay, after all his struggling had settled down with Robbie. William, as usual, was in a world of his own with his thoughts.

It was getting dark as the boat made its way over the water.

"How long are you going to keep up this farce?" asked John Fisken looking across at John Gifford, who sat opposite him in the boat.

"What farce?" questioned John Gifford.

"You know," said John Fisken disgustedly, "you and Barbara and this secret marriage."

"Not long now," John declared triumphantly, "I am getting a house from Uncle Andrew, so we can stay there."

John Fisken went white. "You mean you are leaving Busta House?" he asked incredulously.

"Yes," said John. "It will be better for everyone. My mother has no love for Barbara, and I cannot bear to see the way she is treated. On our own, we will be able to live in peace. My wife and I," he added.

John Fisken could tolerate it no longer. He rose from his seat, and, bringing his hand down heavily on John's face, slapped him across the mouth.

"Your wife," he yelled at John, "she should have been mine. If she stays at Wethersta, I shall never see her." He made as if to hit John again, but John Gifford was ready for him, and this time gave John Fisken such a knock, it landed him in the sea.

"Don't you dare talk about my wife again," John yelled at him. "James, turn the boat around."

Robbie and William endeavoured to fish John out of the water. Hay sat looking on, not sure what to do, and wondering why the two men were quarrelling over Barbara.

John Fisken was a dead weight with sodden clothes and boots full of water. He did not seem to be helping himself either. Then the boys noticed a cut on his head where he must have hit it on going overboard. He was unconscious.

All their efforts were in vain to pull the body on board again. Suddenly, they heard a rasping sound under the boat and it started to keel over. Hay was terrified and clung to John. "It's the seals," he shouted, "it's the seals."

The boys standing in the boat were tipped out. James, Hay and John trying to rescue them also went overboard. The boat righted itself.

None of the men could swim, and even if they had tried, their weighted boots would have hindered them.

They flailed their arms about and shouted for help, but they were not near enough land for anyone to hear. What their last thoughts were, we will never know.

......

Sunday morning dawned clear and bright and Busta House looked a picture in the early morning sunlight.

Cattle in the fields had begun to graze after stretching their legs. The Busta maids were busy lighting fires and preparing breakfast.

"Betty," said Thomas Gifford as he yawned on waking, "I dreamed last night I had lost my staff. It is time I was looking after my lads."

Coming downstairs to breakfast as usual, Thomas was surprised to find none of the boys at the table.

"Barbara, where is James?" he asked.

"I am afraid I do not know, sir," she replied.

"Then find out," shouted Lady Busta coming into the room at that moment.

"Yes, Ma'am," whispered Barbara as she went to the kitchen. She too was worried, John had not come upstairs to her last night.

"Martha," she shouted, "where is everyone? James has not been seen and none of the men. Oh, Martha what could have happened?" and she broke down and wept.

Cathy, the message girl, came by the house just then. Martha ran out to meet her, wringing her hands.

"Cathy, Master John and family and James are missing. Have you heard anything?"

"No," replied Cathy, "they are maybe still at Wethersta. Then looking at a pony on the road she exclaimed, "but that's Master Hay's Frisky. What is he doing here?"

"Here comes Angus from the Brae farm, we'll get him to take the pony and go to Wethersta and see if the party left last night," said Martha.

She went into the house and told Lady Busta what she had done.

"Take me upstairs Barbara to the sitting-room. I shall watch out of the window in case they arrive with the boat." said her Ladyship.

"Yes Ma'am," Barbara whispered.

"I trust John is safe," said Lady Busta with feeling.

"So do I Ma'am," agreed Barbara in tears.

"What do you mean? So do you. How insolent can you be?" shouted the woman. "Go and get on with your work," she waved her hand, dismissing Barbara.

When Angus returned he brought the dreaded news that the boat had left Wethersta with all on board, about midnight.

There was consternation in the household. Search parties were organised at once to scan the shores of the Voe and the isles of Roe and Linga. The boat was soon found with no sign of its occupants. The boat was upright in the water with John's hat and stick still under the seat.

No more could be done that day as it was becoming dark. Messengers were sent to Delting and Northmavine and some to Yell. There were many boats searching and those on foot lined the shore.

78

The men started to dredge early next day. During the day, a man named Johnson and his crew brought the body of John Gifford to the surface. The dredge had caught him by the thumb.

John Gifford's body was laid on the little beach below the booth, near the harbour, where a crowd had gathered.

Barbara Pitcairn left the house as soon as she saw the boat approach the beach. Heedless of Lady Busta's shouts, she reached the crowd and, upon learning that it was John's body which had been recovered, pushed through the crowd and knelt beside him.

"John, oh John, why did you have to die?" she cried as she gave him a last hug and kissed his cold lips, before she took a paper from his inside pocket which she concealed in her dress.

Rising, she made her way to the house again.

"Barbara, what is wrong?" Martha queried as she stumbled into the kitchen.

"They have found John. He is lying dead on the beach," she cried.

"Oh no Barbara, and you liked John so much," Martha added. "What can I do for you?"

"Tell Lady Busta I have fallen sick and cannot attend her today."

"Go to bed," said kind Martha, seeing the state the poor girl was in, "I'll bring you something hot before her Ladyship hears the news, then I shall attend to her."

Barbara went upstairs, and, shutting the door, took the paper she had rescued from John's body and read it. It was their marriage certificate. Hearing Martha at the door, she hurriedly put the paper back into her pocket again.

"Drink that," said Martha. "You will be fine in a while. Now I must go."

Barbara could not believe that she would never see John alive again. As she sat on the side of the bed, she started to cry. Great, heaving sobs. It was pitiful, no-one to comfort her. How she longed for John's arms around her. But she cried also for the little one she was carrying. If only John could have arranged things between him and his uncle before, they could have been living in Wethersta now, together.

When Barbara told John one night that she was expecting his baby, John was determined to find a home of their own soon, as he could not bear to think of what might happen to Barbara at Busta House should his mother find out about the marriage, and the baby.

......

Thomas Gifford, after the death of his sons, was shattered. He had had such high hopes for them. All the training that he had given John and Robbie. Now William was showing a much more positive attitude to business than the other two. And young Hay, what could he say of him? How he had loved that boy. Many times when life was unbearable at the house, he and Hay would go off riding together or walk among the hills round the house.

Of all the fourteen children Thomas and Elizabeth had brought into the world, only three married daughters remained. The eldest was a widow.

Chapter 17

BARBARA's CONFESSION

Thomas Gifford grieved sorely for his four sons. If her Ladyship grieved, she concealed the fact by busying herself with John's funeral. She made all the arrangements herself as her husband seemed incapable of thinking about anything.

Four sons – John 30, Robbie 22, William 18 and young Hay only 15 years.

For Lady Busta it was John she grieved over, her favourite.

The days passed slowly after the funeral. Thomas had to apply for another grieve. James had been with him many years and knew exactly the wishes of his master. It would take some time to train another man in his stead.

Meantime, seeing the awkward situation that the Laird of Busta was in, Angus, from a nearby farm in Brae offered to help. James was in the process of training a young lad, Charles, so he also helped.

Martha grieved for the boys in her own way, she had known them all their lives.

Barbara could no longer keep the marriage and expected baby a secret, so she told Martha. Martha was aghast when told the news.

"I knew you liked Master John – but getting married to him, well," and poor Martha was lost for words.

"And I am expecting his baby," sobbed Barbara.

"You what?" asked Martha incredulously, "how on earth are you going to tell her Ladyship? She will be furious. She never knew John loved any woman but her, she is so selfish. Some say she fancied Miss Henderson of Gardie for him, but kept making excuses that she was not good enough for him.

"So that's the story – well I do not envy you when you tell Lady Elizabeth your news! Have you got proof of the wedding?" asked Martha doubtfully.

"Of course I have," Barbara assured her, "here it is. When John was laid on the beach, I took this out of his pocket," and so saying, she showed Martha the certificate.

"You better tell the Mistress soon," Martha advised, "while her mind is still on John. If she thinks the baby really belonged to John, she may accept it."

The following day Barbara dressed in her best frock and, going in to dine with the Giffords felt very conspicuous. There were four empty chairs at the table.

After the others had left the table, Barbara plucked up courage and spoke to her mistress.

"Ma'am, I have something to tell you," she managed to say in a quivering voice.

"Go ahead then girl," demanded Lady Busta, making the poor girl tremble.
"Don't keep me in suspense."

Barbara, a girl of spirit was determined to tell the woman everything.

"Ma'am I have in my pocket a certificate. It is for the marriage of your son John and myself," she said in a clear, unhurried voice.

"Give that to me," demanded Elizabeth. "What nonsense is this? I shall speak to the Master, and you shall leave my house immediately. Do you hear?"

"But Ma'am, I am with child, and it is John's," continued the girl spiritedly.

Lady Busta sat back in her chair, "I can't believe what I am hearing," she whispered to herself, "I just do not believe it," she screamed. "You of all people, the one I gave a home to, fed and clothed you as one of my own, and yet you can do this to me."

Rising, she struck Barbara across the face and stalked out of the room, leaving the poor girl to pick up the certificate and herself, bruised and crying.

Barbara went to the kitchen where Martha bathed her face. The poor pretty little girl of only sixteen, who had had no happy life apart from the times when Lady Busta was not around, thought she was going to die.

"Go to your room," said Martha and get on some old clothes, then go up the hill to the hen-house and clean out the house. That way her Ladyship won't be able to see you for a while."

On the way there, Barbara stopped and spoke to Beth.

"Whatever has happened?" Beth asked. "Your face is all bruised. How did you hurt it?"

"I'll tell you," said Barbara, so relieved to find a friend to relate her story to.

Beth stood there dumbfounded. "So you really were married to John? That will not please Lady Busta. And you are expecting his child?"

"It all depends," answered Barbara, "if they accept that the certificate is legal, and the baby is John's, they will maybe let me stay."

"I do trust they will," said Beth, who had always liked Barbara and felt she should have had a better deal in life, than be treated the way she had at Busta House. "If you need help any time, let me know. I will always hear news from Cathy," said Beth leaving.

......

Lady Busta walked into her husband's study, "I have heard tales before, but this one beats all. Barbara Pitcairn had the audacity to come to me an hour ago and tell me that she holds a certificate of marriage between her and our son John."

"Where is the certificate?" asked Thomas quietly.

"I threw it back at her," spat out Elizabeth.

"I need to see it," persisted Thomas, "to make sure it is legal."

"No-one will ever see it," snapped the angry woman, "that girl would spin a yarn to anyone and try to get away with it. But she will not fool me, and – that is not the end of the story – listen to this," said Elizabeth standing in a defiant manner. "She says she is also with child to John."

Thomas put his head in his hands, too overcome to speak.

"I will send her in for you to deal with," was Lady Busta's parting shot as she left the room.

When Barbara returned from the hill, Martha told her she was to report to the Master's study at once.

"Oh, Martha, what if they tell me to leave, what can I do?" said the distraught girl.

"Just dress yourself nicely and tell the Master what you told her," advised Martha kindly.

Barbara took care to look neat and tidy, then going downstairs, she knocked on the study door.

"Come in," said Thomas Gifford. As Barbara entered the room, Thomas thought he had never seen the young girl looking so beautiful before. He had always admired her.

"Sit down," he began, his voice quavering, "Babbie, Babbie," he said slowly, "what story is this the Mistress has been telling me. Repeat what you told her."

Barbara took a small lace handkerchief from her pocket and dabbed her eyes.

"Sir," she said, "I must ask your forgiveness for what I am about to tell you. When Master John and I first saw each other, there seemed to be a bond between us. We often met in secret and knew we loved each other. John wanted us to get married, but knowing how much his mother disliked me, he decided to have a secret wedding at Whalsay when Lady Symbister was away at Sumburgh. I took the certificate from John's pocket the day he was drowned.

"John was to ask his Uncle Andrew on the Saturday, at Wethersta, for a house to rent and we would stay there. In that way, it would not upset her Ladyship if I was not living in this house. I am with child to John, and when he knew this, he was all the more determined to get the house. But he has gone now." At this Barbara broke down and cried.

"But Babbie, why did you not come and tell me?" queried Thomas.

"It was the Mistress, she would never have allowed it," sobbed Barbara.

"That is all now, you may go." and Thomas dismissed her.

'John,' he thought, 'I do not blame you for loving this girl, but you could at least have done things above board and confided in me.'

......

After dinner that evening as Thomas and his wife sat in the drawing-room together, so empty now without the boys, Thomas said to his wife, "Betty, why do you not believe Barbara's story? She and John were very fond of one another, anyone could see that. I never dreamed they would act as they have done. If you had not been so hard on the girl, they might have confided in us," remonstrated her husband. "If George Pitcairn had lived, and become the prosperous merchant and ship-owner he certainly would have become, you would have been the first to choose Barbara as a prospective wife for your beloved John."

"That is unfair, Thomas," said Elizabeth petulantly, "I did what I could for the girl."

"You made a servant out of her," answered Thomas and continued to smoke his pipe in silence, while Elizabeth gazed into the fire with her thoughts.

Chapter 18

GIDEON

As Barbara's confinement drew near, she spent what little spare time she could get knitting small clothes for her baby.

Lady Busta employed Beth again to take Barbara's place but she had to work until the last day. The day before the baby came, Barbara had an unfortunate accident. She had rung the gong for dinner and was hurrying along the corridor to her room. Rushing past the sitting-room door she met Lady Busta emerging, like a ship in full sail! Knocking Barbara over, she did not wait to see if she was all right, but continued down the stairs to dinner.

Barbara lay quite a while, till Beth, coming up the stairs to put peats on the fire, found her lying on the floor.

"Are you all right, Barbara?" she asked in a terrified tone, "whatever happened to you?"

"I was knocked down by her Ladyship on her way to dinner. Beth, I think I feel pains starting. What shall I do?" said the alarmed girl.

"I will take you to your room and then tell Martha. She will not be able to attend you until the meal is finished. Just get to bed," and Beth ran downstairs to the kitchen unable to comprehend how cruel Lady Busta could be.

Beth decided to sleep in Barbara's room that night. It was just as well. The contractions had started at 8pm and were getting really bad. Beth ran downstairs to tell Martha, who, practical woman that she was, had seen to it that the range was kept well heated for hot water, in case of any development in the night.

About 2 am, Beth was really in distress, the baby was big, and she, being small, made it a difficult birth. With no doctor handy, Martha did the best she could. At 4 am Barbara Pitcairn's child was born – a healthy boy!

Martha sent Beth to look after things in the household, it was unknown to the Laird and his wife, that a baby had been born in the house that night. Martha settled Barbara as best she could and left her very weak to have a rest while she attended to the baby. He was a lovely boy and Martha was so proud of him. He was just like his father as she remembered him. That seemed a long time ago now. But she must not daydream, there was plenty to do.

"Where is Martha?" Lady Busta demanded to know when Beth took the eggs and toast in for breakfast.

"Ma'am, she is attending to Barbara," said Beth.

"Well, tell her to come and attend to me first," shouted Elizabeth.

"Ma'am," started Beth.

"Go at once girl, when you are told," Elizabeth snapped.

"Betty, Betty, could you not listen to the girl? She was going to explain something," chided Thomas.

Martha appeared at the dining-room door, a bit dishevelled. "Yes, Ma'am, you sent for me," she said in as even a voice as she could.

"What is the meaning of this? Sending Beth to attend at the table. Where were you?" she asked.

"If Ma'am will allow me, I will explain," began Martha. "In the night, Barbara Pitcairn gave birth to a baby boy. The baby is fine, but Barbara is not well. Will you please give me permission to fetch a doctor?"

"A boy, I see" mused Elizabeth, "a boy.... No, certainly not, she has brought this on herself, so she can take the consequences. Get on with your household chores."

Barbara was not well, but her Ladyship would not hear of calling the doctor for a servant. Beth did well – her work and most of Martha's. Martha spent a lot of time with Barbara trying to coax her to drink a little soup and milk, for her and the baby's sake.

Meanwhile, Lady Busta's thoughts were dwelling on the certificate. If Barbara showed it to Thomas, he would no doubt agree that it was valid, and Barbara would be able to stay in the house. If Thomas died, she Barbara, would be in charge of the house with her son and heir.

Elizabeth was determined to find the certificate and burn it, if it was the last thing she did. She had to wait a few days more.

One afternoon when Elizabeth was in the house alone, she crept up to Barbara's room. On finding her and the baby asleep, she began to look through the few possessions the girl had in the room. Ah, yes, the certificate was in her skirt pocket!

Hiding it in her own pocket, the older woman crept from the room to her own bedroom where she had a chest-of-drawers which had a concealed compartment behind one of them.

Putting the certificate in a bundle of other papers, she shut the drawer and patted the chest.

'Everything is safe now,' she said to herself. 'No-one will ever find that as long as I live.'

......

The baby grew each day and Barbara began to feel a bit stronger, but she never really felt well as she had no proper attention after the birth, and was weak and tired.

One morning, Lady Busta told Martha to tell Barbara to come to the study with the baby. Martha delivered the message.

Barbara broke down in tears, "This will be to tell us to go," she sobbed. "Help me to get dressed Martha, I still feel so weak."

Putting on her blouse and skirt, Barbara put her hand in her pocket to touch the certificate, but it was gone.

"Martha," she almost yelled, "my marriage certificate, it's not here. Has anyone been in my room? I can trust you and Beth, but who else could have known it was there?"

"I don't know, Barbara, we will look for it when you come up again, but you better go now. I have got baby ready," said Martha handing over the small bundle.

"Thank you Martha, you are such a kind friend. He is wearing the lovely shawl which you made. I am so glad," said Barbara going to the door.

"Take care on the stairs," was Martha's parting words. Barbara reached the study door and stood for a long time till she heard a voice ringing out, "Where is that girl? I don't have all day to waste on her".

Tapping the door gently, Barbara entered.

"Sir, Ma'am," she said and curtseyed as best she could.

Thomas, looking at her saw a young mother, fresh from childbirth, with a sad yet lovely smile on her face as she looked at her baby son.

"Come over here girl," said Lady Busta, "we can't see the baby properly over there."

"Yes Ma'am," said the girl moving nearer to Thomas. He smiled at her. How beautiful she looked, yet so vulnerable and not to be rasped at by his wife.

Lady Busta must have softened a little as she gazed at the small boy. She had no intention of holding him, but put her finger on his forehead and said to Thomas, "That brow should make a man of him!"

"You may leave now," she told Barbara, a catch in her throat, the baby seemed to have touched a cord in her that she thought had long been forgotten.

......

Looking from the sitting-room window a few weeks later, Lady Busta recognised one of her husband's gigs approaching the driveway.

It was not long until Martha knocked to announce the visitor. "Mr Scott, Ma'am," said Martha.

Elizabeth was very pleased to see him and ordered afternoon tea. "Thomas, she informed her visitor, will not be long coming, he has gone on a visit to Brae."

When Thomas appeared he persuaded Mr Scott to stay the night. Martha was asked to set an extra place at the table.

In the drawing-room, after the meal, Mr Scott said, "Last time I visited you, you had one of George Pitcairn's girls staying with you. Is she still here?"

Thomas and Elizabeth looked at each other, then Elizabeth said in a rather strained voice, "Yes, she is, but I am afraid she is in disgrace. She had a baby, and of all the ridiculous nonsense, she insists that John is the father!"

"I would love to see him," said Mr Scott. "George was one of my dearest friends and I missed him so much after his death."

"Very well," agreed Thomas, "we shall tell Barbara to bring him in." He rang the bell and gave Martha the message.

It was not long before Barbara and the baby came in.

"Good evening, Barbara," greeted Scott rising to meet the young mother, "I believe this is your son."

"Yes, sir," Barbara blushed.

"May I hold him, please?" asked Mr Scott, "Grandson of my dear friend George. He is not a Pitcairn though. He is the image of your John, Elizabeth, at this age."

"Do you really think so?" she asked excitedly, and in an unguarded moment added, "Yes, that brow and chin. Strangely enough, I had a dream last night," she continued, as if in a trance, "my son John appeared to me and he said, 'Mother you are not to grieve too much over me, there is still a remnant left.'"

She stood staring for a second, then, realising what she had said, gave a curt, "Thank you," to Barbara, and dismissed her with a glance.

When Mr Scott had gone from the room, Elizabeth and Thomas looked at each other. "Do you think she is really telling the truth, that she was secretly married to John?" asked Thomas hopefully.

"Nonsense," Lady Busta dismissed all thought of it from their minds.

Thinking of the hidden document upstairs, she added, "I cannot bear to look at the woman."

......

Each day after that Martha brought the baby for the Giffords to see. The child was growing older and the Laird insisted he get christened. Arrangements were duly made. Thomas and Elizabeth went to the church in Olnafirth by boat with Angus. Many of the family had been married, christened, and buried there.

88

As soon as the Laird's boat had left, Barbara took her little boy whom she secretly called 'John' and, leaving by the big studded front door, walked down the Willow Walk and through the wrought-iron gates to the road.

Although Barbara hated the water, she was glad to be in the boat on her own with Peter, the new boatman.

"Will you be all right there Ma'am," he asked, "there is a rug for you I brought."

Barbara could hardly believe her ears, being called Ma'am, and Peter so thoughtful of her. If her father had lived, she mused, this is what my life really would be like.

The baby was very quiet throughout the proceedings. When the time came for the christening, the Minister called the party to the font and Thomas stepped over to Barbara, much to her surprise. He took the baby in his hands and held it up saying, "Gideon Gifford!"

Barbara gave a little gasp. So Thomas Gifford did believe her story. She shut her eyes and thanked God. Lady Busta glancing at her thought she would faint, but not so, Barbara Pitcairn was a spirited youngster in spite of all she had been through. As Barbara opened her eyes again Lady Busta saw an almost peaceful look on the young mother's face. Gideon had been accepted as John's son. He would be well looked after and brought up as a gentleman. Barbara did not mind what became of her life now, she had done her utmost for her beloved child.

Thomas Gifford handed the boy back to his mother again and the service ended.

Barbara's joy knew no bounds as she cuddled her little boy in the boat as it took them back to Busta House.

"What are you calling the boy, Ma'am?" asked Peter kindly.

"Gideon," the girl replied.

"Fine name that - Gideon Pitcairn." Peter tried the name out.

"No, Peter, the Laird named him, Gideon Gifford," she answered proudly.

As the Gifford's boat touched the pier at Busta, Angus jumped onto the steps to secure the rope.

Thomas alighted first then helped his wife out of the boat and up the steps.

Peter helped Barbara and the baby out of their boat, and they made their way up the pier also.

By this time, Thomas had opened the large wrought-iron gates for Elizabeth and she continued up the path to the house. Still holding the gate open, Thomas said to Barbara, who was going to make her way round the wall to the back door, "No, Barbara, come this way – Gideon Gifford is going to enter Busta House by the front door!"

"Thank you, sir," Barbara said blushing.

They walked up the Willow Walk together in silence. As they approached the front door, Thomas stopped.

"Take my staff," he ordered in an emotional voice, " I will take the child."

Handing over the baby, Barbara took the Laird's staff in exchange. As Thomas crossed the threshold of the door, he held the boy in his hands and said,

"Gideon Gifford, Busta House is your home."

Then he handed the baby back to his mother to care for.

Martha, appearing at that moment took in the situation. Nothing could have pleased her more, but that the youngster would be recognised as one of the family.

......

Barbara did not keep well and many a day Beth was called in to do her chores.

Gideon grew into a fine boy, with the love of his mother and healthy living. He possessed a sweet and amiable disposition and was liked by all who met him.

Thomas and Elizabeth adopted him into the family as son and heir, the only remaining representative of the eight sons.

Lady Busta had taken to Gideon from the start and Thomas, now an ageing man, was extremely fond of the boy. He was determined, no doubt, due partly to his wife's instigation, to make Gideon heir to his estate.

Chapter 19

CHRISTINA

In spite of the recent tragic boating accident, life at Busta House carried on. Many friends and neighbours called to sympathise and offer their condolences, among them was John Bruce of Symbister. His wife sent her respects, but, owing to ill-health, felt unable to make the ferry crossing as it would not be to her advantage.

One morning, a few months later, Thomas Gifford received a black-edged envelope.

"Who can this be now?" he questioned.

Opening the envelope slowly he read of the forthcoming funeral of Lady Symbister.

Poor Thomas, after all he had suffered lately, here was the death of the wife of his good friend John. How does one comfort in times like these?

Thomas rose from his desk, and taking the letter, went upstairs to the sitting-room where Elizabeth was discussing the meals for the day with cook.

"Could you come back in a moment?" she asked her husband in a somewhat irritable tone.

"I'm afraid not, my dear," Thomas answered, "this is important."

"You may go," Elizabeth told cook, "come back in ten minutes time."

Thomas sat down in an armchair looking white and drawn.

"Read this," he said, handing the letter to his wife.

As Elizabeth sat at her desk she scanned the letter.

"But Thomas," she began, "John was here only last week and he never mentioned anything seriously wrong with Lady Symbister. Her death must have come suddenly. John will be very lonely on his own."

Thomas left early next day for Whalsay. Peter took him in the boat as far as Olnafirth where he hired a pony to take him to Laxo Voe to catch the ferry.

It was a beautiful day, it seemed so sad to be thinking of death when everything around the countryside was bathed in sunshine.

Lamb was waiting for Thomas Gifford when he arrived, to drive him to the house. John Bruce met him at the door, not waiting for Thomas to be ushered in. As they entered the library John said, "I am so glad you were able to come," and he wept. Thomas laid a hand on his shoulder to comfort his friend, "The Lord hath given," he quoted, "the Lord hath taken away."

"Blessed be the name of the Lord," whispered John. "I trust I shall be as brave as you."

He ordered tea to be brought in and the two men conversed about funeral proceedings.

After the funeral was over, Thomas took leave of John who insisted on coming in the gig to the boat to see his friend away. It seemed he was loathe to go back to the empty house on his own.

Each month after this, Thomas invited John Bruce to stay for a week with his family at Busta House. Although the family had been depleted by the loss of nine children, it was still a busy household.

Coming to the house so frequently, John Bruce lost a lot of his lonely feelings as he went with Thomas fishing or shooting. Young Patrick Gifford of Ollaberry, Thomas' nephew, sometimes joined them.

......

Christina was very artistic. She often looked up from her sketching to find John Bruce standing behind her chair watching with interest the developing picture of a flower or scene. He would compliment the artist, much to her embarrassment, and she would blush. At meal-times John was always attentive to Christina making sure she had a taste from each dish provided.

Although Christina admired John Bruce, she realised that that admiration was slowly turning to love for this kind, gentle man, who, getting over his own bereavement, had helped her father to come to terms with his.

One lovely evening John plucked up the courage to ask his friend Thomas if he could take Christina a walk by the shore.

"I shall have to ask Lady Busta's opinion first," said Thomas, and when her Ladyship agreed, he was able to tell John that his request had been granted.

The couple left by the front door and walked slowly down the Willow Walk. Lady Busta rushed to the window of the sitting-room upstairs to make sure that the couple neither touched hands, or lingered to chat! She need not have worried as their behaviour was exemplary.

"I think they make a lovely pair, don't you?" Elizabeth asked her husband as he came into the room.

"I am glad you think so," was the relieved reply.

As John and Christina's romance blossomed, there was talk of a quiet wedding. Neither family wanted anything special as it was only two years since they had been bereaved.

The wedding, to which a few friends and relatives had been invited, was held in Busta House. Cook made a lovely spread which everyone enjoyed.

The following day, the couple left Busta House and made their way to Whalsay. Christina was now Lady Symbister! Lady Busta agreed that Alice would go with her daughter, as a companion.

Barbara and Alice were very upset at being parted, but Barbara was happy for her sister to be with Lady Symbister as she knew she would be treated kindly.

Barbara continued to look after Lady Busta's needs. Coping with a small child at the same time meant that she had little spare time for herself. Gideon was a good, contented boy and loved going with his mother to feed the hens or walk to the cottages to collect knitted goods for the Booth. Needless to say, Barbara loved these times too, when she could tell her son the names of all the wild flowers and birds.

Chapter 20

A VISIT TO SYMBISTER

"There is a letter from your brother John at Westshore," Thomas informed his wife, "he has kindly invited me to stay with him and his wife when I go next week to Tingwall for the court. I shall go across in the ferry to Whalsay and see John and Christina for a day and thence take a ferry to Lerwick. I wish I could take Jasper with me, the Shetland ponies are so small, but they are very sure-footed and always willing to carry the heaviest person sitting on them. Have you anything you wish me to take to Whalsay when I go?"

Turning to Barbara he said, "I shall see your sister Alice also. Have you a message for her?"

"If I write a letter, sir, would you be so kind as to give it to her? It is her birthday in two days time and I have knitted her a pair of lace stockings."

"Yes, Barbara, I shall be glad to take your message for you," answered Thomas.

Lady Busta sent a jar of her best strawberry jam to Christina as it was her favourite.

Barbara had not seen her sister since they were separated but heard from time to time that she was well treated in her position. Barbara, being a generous-hearted girl was glad Alice had gone to Whalsay and she had stayed at Busta. She would not have liked her sister to go through what she had experienced.

The day for Thomas' departure was fine and he set off on Jasper.

"May I accompany you to Brae?" asked Barbara, "I can take Jasper home again."

"That would be fine, thanks Barbara," replied Thomas. "Look after Lady Busta while I am away. I look forward to seeing those chair-covers finished soon!"

Thomas was very fond of Barbara and was saddened that his wife had so little time for her. Maybe that would change now that they would be working together on the embroideries.

As they parted at Brae, Barbara handed her parcel to Thomas. "I wish I was going too," she said, "but please give my regards to Lady Symbister and Alice."

"I shall," replied Thomas handing over the reins to the young girl. "Take care of yourself."

Barbara was not one to show her feelings, but as she took the reins, tears sprang to her eyes and she hastily rubbed them away. Thomas put a hand on her shoulder, "Don't worry," he said kindly, "I shall see that you spend a few days with your sister soon."

"Thank you sir, I would enjoy that," smiled Barbara.

Barbara took her time going back to the stables. It was lovely, trotting along, breathing in the pure air and relaxing in the warm sunshine. Wild flowers were out in profusion along the sides of the path.

......

When Thomas Gifford arrived in Whalsay, Lamb, the butler, was down to meet him at the ferry with the gig.

"Good day, sir, you have certainly chosen a fine day for the crossing," he greeted Thomas.

"Yes, Lamb," agreed Thomas. "Anything new on the island?" he queried.

"The fishing is good at the moment and the Booth has acquired a number of fascinating goods from the continent," supplied Lamb.

Christina eagerly greeted her father. "It is good to see you again, and looking so well. How is Mother? She did not mention her health when she wrote about your visit."

"She is fine, thank you," replied Thomas. "Ah, Alice. How are you my dear?" he said turning to the young lady approaching him.

"I am well, thank you. Have you news of Barbara? I fear she misses our mother greatly," she added.

"I have a gift for you from her," Thomas told her, "it is in my portmanteau."

"Barbara is always thinking of other people," Alice said with a quiver in her voice, "she would do anything to help anyone. She must fret so about mother."

"I think Barbara is taking good care of her," supplied Thomas, handing Alice her gift. "She is a very accomplished young lady."

Christina rang the bell for tea, as the party were now in the sitting-room.

"Mother sent a pot of your favourite jam," Thomas said handing it to his daughter, "She says the fruit has been plentiful this year."

"I must write to thank her," Christina said taking the proferred jar. "No-one makes jam like Harriet."

"How is Barbara settling in at Busta House?" Christina asked.

"Fine, fine," Thomas answered a bit hesitantly, "she is presently helping your mother to finish the cushion covers for the dining-room chairs. They will look magnificent when completed. She has great talent and has been taught by Martha to spin and knit the fine, lace stockings."

"Lady Symbister, just look at what Barbara has sent me!" shouted an excited Alice. "Shetland lace hose. Aren't they beautiful?"

"Oh, Alice," enthused her Ladyship, "they are exquisite!"

Turning to Thomas she asked, "Do you mean to tell me that Barbara has knitted these herself?"

"My dear," answered Thomas proudly, "she not only knitted them, but collected the wool from the field, spun it and knitted the stockings. Her spinning is so fine, believe me, those threads are double thickness. She gave your Mother and me a demonstration one evening."

"I wish I could knit like that," moaned Alice, "then I would sell the hose to help Mother."

"That is exactly what Barbara is doing, my child. You are both good girls thinking of your mother as you do. I am sure she appreciates it," ended Thomas.

Thomas visited the Hanseatic Booth next day and marvelled at some of the foreign articles brought over in the boats. He bought a pair of fur gloves for Elizabeth his wife. Picking up a couple of small lace handkerchiefs, made in France, he bought them for Barbara and Alice.

After a pleasant couple of days in Whalsay, Thomas joined a boat going to Lerwick. This was a large six-oared boat which took a number of passengers and much goods.

As the boat approached the little pier at Lerwick, Thomas saw a row of Shetland ponies waiting to take passengers on their way. He himself, was to spend a night in the town before going on to Scalloway. A young lad offered to carry his portmanteau on his pony for a shilling, Thomas followed the boy to the hotel after paying the boatman £1.16 for his fare.

A visit to the court-house was essential, so while in town Thomas walked along the busy street to the Tolbooth. Two cases were to be held that afternoon so Thomas Gifford presided over them. Later, relaxing after a substantial meal of hot soup and roast lamb, he wondered if he should pay a call on Mrs Pitcairn. Her husband had been a close friend of his.

But on second thoughts he felt it wiser to leave the visit meantime, as she may have heard in a roundabout way of his wife's treatment of her daughter, and he had no desire to get involved. Instead, he had a look in the shop windows and compared the prices to those in the store at home.

Chapter 21

WEDDING ARRANGEMENTS

If Lady Busta enjoyed anything, it was a wedding in the family! She relished the thought of her youngest daughter Andrina, being of marriageable age. A wedding could soon be in the offing.

Young Patrick Gifford of Ollaberry had been frequenting Busta House lately, to go shooting with his Uncle Thomas who missed his sons' company badly. Patrick was son of Andrew Gifford of Ollaberry, youngest brother of Thomas. Patrick was a handsome young man, mannerly and friendly. He was obviously attracted to Andrina and she returned his attentions.

When Thomas and Patrick returned from an afternoon on the hills, Elizabeth would be pleased to ask the lad to stay for a meal with them. During the after-dinner conversation in the drawing-room, Andrina entertained Patrick with stories of her now deceased brothers and the happy times they had shared together. Elizabeth was grateful to see Thomas more relaxed as he talked with the young man on different matters.

The romance budded and soon the young couple were engaged.

It was now five years since the tragic loss of their sons and Thomas and Elizabeth welcomed a challenge in the ordinary, everyday course of life. Something to bring a freshness and brightness to their future. There was much to be arranged for the wedding and Elizabeth, looking out a book from her bureau, began a long list of guests to invite.

There were relations from around the islands and of course the 'continent', as Thomas called the mainland of Britain.

Barbara was asked to make the bride's and bridesmaid's dresses. It was not a job Lady Busta enjoyed asking the girl to do, but it would be much cheaper, she reckoned, than employing a seamstress especially to make the garments.

On a visit to her daughter, Lady Symbister in Whalsay, Elizabeth visited the Hanseatic booth and found, to her pleasure, that they had recently received a bale of the most luxurious white satin, also one of duck-egg blue. Her joy knew no bounds as she discovered white swan down with which to edge the dresses.

Christina helped her Mother with many other purchases for the wedding. Remembering her own one, she trusted Andrina's would be as happy.

Barbara was a careful and very neat seamstress, having been taught sewing when young. She enjoyed embroidery and tapestry. Nowadays she knitted to make money to help herself in the future.

Many a time as she sat in the sewing room, Barbara would hold the white dress up in front of her and gaze into the mirror.

Tears dimmed her eyes as she imagined it might have been her own frock. She and Andrina were about the same size so Barbara was often asked to put the dress on so that Andrina could see exactly how it looked. The young bride-to-be was thrilled with Barbara's work and amazed at the skill with which her friend sewed small pearl buttons on to the bodice in a pattern, or gathered smocking at the waist. Small buttons were covered and sewn on to the cuffs and down the back of the frock opening. The skirt ended in a flowing train, to which tiny loops were attached with which to hold it up when walking along or dancing.

Extra material was purchased and sent off to London to a firm who specialised in making satin covered shoes.

An Edinburgh firm supplied hats, gloves and parasols.

Lady Busta ordered many dresses to be sent from London shops so that she could choose which one suited her. Thomas also sported a new outfit, and looked very smart, though, truth to tell, he would rather have worn his 'comfortable tweeds'!

......

Andrina was very upset because her mother refused to let Barbara be her bridesmaid. "Mother," she pleaded, "Barbara has been my friend for years and I promised she would be my bridesmaid."

"You can choose anyone you like apart from her," said Elizabeth, "Barbara will not be your bridesmaid."

"Can I have Alice then?" queried the despondent girl.

"Of course you may," Elizabeth replied relieved, "I think it would be too much for Barbara anyway," she added, remembering the marriage certificate upstairs. She sighed. Why had she not shown the certificate to Thomas at the time? She had been too proud to admit that Barbara really was John's wife.

As Andrina's wedding approached, she and Barbara went for a ride, away from the hustle and bustle at the house.

"Barbara," began Andrina hesitantly, "you know I have always said I would have you as my bridesmaid? I have asked Mother several times, but she refuses and says I can have anyone else but you."

"Don't worry, Andrina," said Barbara kindly, "I would feel out of place now amongst all the gentry coming. In any case, you need someone who is young and beautiful."

"Barbara, you are the most beautiful and kind person I know," said Andrina, "you have always been so good and helpful to us all."

"It was the least I could do," Barbara said, "when your mother took Alice and me into your home."

"Would you mind very much if I asked Alice then?" queried Andrina.

"Of course not," laughed a relieved Barbara, "I am sure she would love to be asked. She would certainly make a dash with the young men. She will not meet many her age at Symbister."

As the girls rode home after their ride, they passed a young woman with a basket of peats on her back. Her little girl of about three was running ahead of her when she fell and cut her knee quite badly on a sharp stone. She cried pitifully, but her mother could not bend to pick her up because of the heavy load on her back.

Immediately, Barbara dismounted and ran to help the little girl, picking her up and dabbing her sore knee. Lifting her on to her pony, they walked with the woman to her cottage.

"Shall I carry her in for you?" asked Barbara quite naturally. She was used to visiting the crofters cottages when she went to collect the knitted garments for sale in the Booth.

"Coming?" she asked Andrina. At first, the girl scowled and sat still, then, dismounting, she went into the cottage also. Never having been inside one before, she was struck by its smallness. It would go into their long drawing-room, no bother! As she looked around the little room she was appalled at the scant, poor furniture and deplorable state of the place.

Taking a clean handkerchief from her pocket, Barbara put a little water on it from a cup dipped in a bucket. The child was very good and hardly cried, so fascinated was she by the kind lady.

Agnes, the child's mother, had disposed of the peat basket at the fireside and came to comfort her daughter.

"Have you got a piece of cloth to wind round the cut until it heals?" asked Barbara.

"Yes, Ma'am," said the woman, opening a drawer in the wooden dresser, then she handed a piece of cloth to Barbara who wound it round the girl's knee.

"Can you give her some hot soup? She has had a nasty fall," she was asked.

"Sorry, Ma'am," but we had the last of it yesterday. I was going to boil some potatoes for our meal," answered Agnes, "my son, Harold, is away trying to get a fish at the shore."

"We shall see that you do not go hungry," said Andrina finding her tongue at last, "a bag of meal will be sent tonight."

"How can I thank you both enough for all you have done?" sobbed Agnes. "I shall never forget your goodness to us. My husband and two sons were lost at sea two years ago and I have no means of support except my knitting and selling eggs."

"If you have any eggs to sell, we can always do with them," said Andrina warming to this woman who had so little. In fact she was quite proud of herself to think that she could offer help to anyone at all.

It was all thanks to Barbara's kindly influence.

That evening at dinner, while the family ate their meal, poor Andrina burst into tears.

"Whatever is the matter?" asked her mother.

"How can I eat all this food when there are poor folks on our estate who literally have nothing to eat?" she sobbed.

"You do not mean to say Barbara has been carting you around to one of these old cottages to make you sorry for the wretched people there?" shouted Lady Busta.

"No, Mother, it was not like that at all," the indignant daughter replied.

Andrina proceeded to recount the afternoons incident.

"Mother, they have so little," began Andrina, "a stone floor, no furniture to speak of. The woman lost her husband and two sons at sea, two years ago. She still has a boy of about twelve and a girl of three, Annie. Mother, you would love her. She reminded me very much of our Elizabeth in the painting you often show me, when she was small. I am afraid I took the liberty of saying we could do with some eggs. I hope you do not mind?"

"Of course not my dear," said Elizabeth kindly.

"We shall have to try and do something about the folks in the district Father," pleaded Andrina.

"Yes dear, after the wedding," said her father with finality.

......

It was arranged that the wedding ceremony would take place in the large drawing-room at Busta House. Invitation cards were handwritten and given to Angus to hand out or post to the recipients.

"Cook is a real genius," Elizabeth commented to Thomas, "she has baked the most beautiful cake for the wedding, and covered it with marzipan and sugar icing. She has saved up the ingredients for weeks to make some delicious desserts. Her most tempting dish, I think, will be our own lamb with redcurrant sauce. We have plenty of lamb and red-currants just now, and the gardener has lifted a quantity of potatoes and other vegetables. We shall have a feast fit for a king! I do not believe either Robert or Patrick Stewart ever dined so sumptuously as we shall!"

"We have been fortunate having Cook all these years," observed Thomas.

"Yes," Elizabeth added, "wait till you see the dainty cakes and tempting dishes."

"Angus has seen to the wines," Thomas said with a twinkle in his eye, "those brought from Oporto by Captain Bull will add greatly to the meal. Of course the German wines are always a favourite. I expect a number of our guests have never tasted any of them. We shall have that new fruit 'orange' for them to try also."

"Do not worry about a thing," Elizabeth smiled, "Cook has it all under control. Remember the wonderful meal she made for Christina's wedding."

"That was fantastic," Thomas replied, remembering the expressions on the faces of the guests as they looked at some of the dishes cook had so skillfully concocted!

"Yes," added Andrina, "Cook was telling me how many eggs she had to get to make sponges, cakes and trifles. I think I am looking forward to the meal as much as anything! I do trust it will be a lovely, warm day. We are having the meals in the garden, Mother?" she queried.

"I do hope so," answered Elizabeth, "it makes serving the food so much easier. Angus has arranged for extra tables, chairs and cutlery, also dishes to be brought in and Martha told me she has looked out all the linen tablecloths and napkins necessary for the occasion. Barbara will be doing the flower arrangements from our own garden. She really excels at floral decorations," added Lady Busta with as much grace as she could muster! "The flowers are plentiful this year and in an amazing riot of colour. I will borrow a podium or two from Christina, but have plenty large vases and containers to fill empty spaces in the house. There will be smaller crystal vases for the tables.

"Martha is polishing the silver candlesticks and the candelabras are sparkling too. How I do love occasions like this when we can show off the silver and crystal! It is so beautiful. We have not had much to celebrate lately so we will make the most of this time with our friends. I do trust many will manage to come."

"Yes," agreed Thomas, "the weather is ideal, I hope it lasts. There may be a few guests from the 'Continent' so we will have to book accommodation for them. Angus is always a help to us there, he knows the inns around and will see to that."

"Getting back to the food again," Andrina began, "Barbara was telling me that three of the cows have calved lately so we shall have plenty of milk and lashings of cream with everything!"

"The strawberries are bountiful this year," added Elizabeth. "Everyone enjoys the Busta House fruit. By the way, cook told Angus to procure a few brace of pheasants from Sandwater. They seem to abound in that area, also pigeons."

The days leading up to the great day were often filled with anxiety. Fortunately Lady Busta, with the help of Barbara, had finished embroidering the twelve dining-room chair covers, also two larger covers for the carver chairs. They looked magnificent and were much admired.

Suits for the men and dresses for the ladies were delivered each time the boat from Leith arrived. Barbara had many adjustments to make on hems of dresses and waists to take in to make the ladies look smaller.

Andrina had seen a length of luxurious, dark green velvet in the Booth and bought it for a suit for Gideon.

Needless to say, poor Barbara was kept sewing all day and well into the night trying to get the garments ready in time.

Gideon's little suit was very smart. He was nearly four years old now and proud of his new outfit. Barbara had really enjoyed fitting, cutting out and sewing the suit. It had been a labour of love. The times spent in measuring up and trying on the garments as they progressed had been most precious to both mother and son. Barbara often longed that John could have seen his son now – the future 'Laird of Busta'. Many a tear was shed as she sewed away silently on her own.

......

One day as Andrina and her mother went for a walk with Pierre, they met Agnes and Annie.

"What a beautiful child," commented her Ladyship.

"Hello Annie," Andrina greeted the little girl. Bending down, she asked how her knee was.

"It is much better now," Annie thanked her.

"Mother, this is Agnes, and her little girl who fell," said Andrina introducing the two women.

"I made this for you," said Annie, shyly handing Andrina a small gift.

"It is a blue garter," said Agnes proudly, "she made it herself."

"Oh, thank you dear," Andrina hugged the child, "you are so sweet. I shall wear this on my wedding day."

"I believe you are supplying us with eggs from time to time," Elizabeth said to Agnes. "We can do with plenty at the moment."

104

"Thank you Ma'am," Agnes bowed, and taking Annie's hand went on their way.

"I see the resemblance to Elizabeth, as you said," observed Lady Busta "but what a poor frock the child was wearing. We must see to it that she gets something better to wear, especially if they are delivering things to the house."

"Yes, Mother," agreed Andrina, smiling to herself.

"You know," continued her mother, "I think I have a few of Elizabeth's little frocks in the attic. I could look them out and give them to Annie."

"But Mother, I thought you were keeping them for sentimental reasons," Andrina said kindly.

"Well I think it is time I thought of these poor people, and give them some help. We have so much, and these clothes mean nothing to anyone but me, and when I am gone – let's look some out tomorrow."

"Mother, that is wonderful," said Andrina giving her arm a squeeze.

Next time Agnes and Annie called at Busta House to deliver eggs, they were handed a large basket to take home.

On arrival at the cottage, Agnes opened the basket excitedly and when she saw the contents she sat down on a chair and burst into tears. "Annie love, come and see what the kind ladies have given us. Lovely frocks, coats, petticoats, bonnets, stockings and shoes, and here are some dresses for me too."

Chapter 22

ANDRINA's WEDDING

The morning of Andrina's wedding dawned bright and sunny. The household had wakened very early and all was bustle and hurry to get everything ready for the great occasion.

Barbara, preparing a breakfast tray for Andrina, was determined to make everything perfect. As she passed one of the many large, lovely flower arrangements on the stairway which she had completed yesterday, she picked a small pink rosebud and put it on the tray. Knocking on the bedroom door, she entered and placed the tray on the bedside table.

"Good morning, Andrina what a lovely day for your wedding."

"Oh, thanks," said the girl sleepily, "you have brought my breakfast, how good of you. What shall I do without you? We have been together for years now, we will always stay friends I trust."

"Of course," assured Barbara, "now take your tea while it is hot."
Barbara bent and placed a kiss on Andrina's forehead.

"God bless you, and I trust you will be very happy," she whispered in as steady a voice as she could.

Once outside the bedroom door, Barbara hurried along the corridor and burst into tears. She did hope her friend would be happy – so why was she crying? It seemed that all the happenings of the past weeks and months of preparation were catching up with her emotions. She was not jealous of her friend in any way, and only wished the best for her, but how wonderful it would have been if her own wedding had been a trifle like this one. She would just have to live on memories. She was not even invited to this wedding.

So deep in her own thoughts was Barbara that she bumped into Martha coming upstairs.

"Whatever is the matter?" Martha asked kindly, "has someone upset you?"

"No Martha," the girl replied, "I was wishing Andrina all the best for today and my emotions got the better of me."

"Dry your eyes now and lay a breakfast tray for her Ladyship," said Martha, feeling action was better than sympathy at this juncture.

Barbara dried her eyes on the corner of her white apron, and headed for the kitchen.

At the foot of the stairs, Thomas, who had been for an early morning ride, met her and looked quite concerned.

"Now Barbara, what has upset you?" he asked, "we should all be happy today."

"Yes, sir," Barbara managed to say, "I was congratulating Andrina on her lovely day and I - I - was overcome."

Thomas put a comforting arm around her and assured her that if it had not been for her help, things would not have gone so smoothly. "And," he added, "you will be at the wedding and will stay near to the bride in case she needs your help. Will you do that?"

"Yes, sir," Barbara smiled.

Barbara felt very happy as she walked to the busy kitchen, but the thought struck her, what was she going to wear?

......

As the wedding guests arrived, Martha met each at the door and took the men's coats and hats, putting them in the Library, along with the ladies parasols, then ushered them into the drawing-room, which was seated for the wedding ceremony.

Patrick and his best man stood at the far end of the room, with the minister in front of them, waiting for the arrival of the bride.

Every eye was on Andrina as she walked slowly, on the arm of her father, to stand beside Patrick. She looked exquisite in the dream of a frock, which even Barbara had to admit was perfect. Her hair was piled on top of her head and held in place by a sparkling tiara. Patrick was very smart in his new suit complete with bow tie.

Alice's dress was a shimmer of blue and she too looked elegant.

Gideon excelled himself in behaviour and poise. He really looked the part and enjoyed admiring glances from everyone!

Barbara followed the party into the room and sat near the front where Thomas Gifford had reserved a chair for her.

After the register was signed, the wedding party trooped out to the garden where laden tables awaited the guests.

Thomas saw to it that Barbara sat beside Gideon as one of the guests. She looked lovely in the pretty frock she had made for her own wedding. There had been no time to do anything for herself, and besides, it reminded her most vividly of her dear John. It seemed as if he were near.

Everyone enjoyed the beautiful meal and various wines.

As evening approached, the guests who had stayed went back to the house where the drawing-room had been cleared ready for dancing. A band of fiddlers had been hired and so, the first of several days celebrations had started. There were also songs, recitations and stories to fill the evenings.

On the fourth day, Patrick took his wife Andrina to her new home on the Ollaberry estate.

Andrina and Barbara were upset at parting, having been close friends for years.

Chapter 23

BARBARA LEAVES BUSTA

Martha had taught Barbara to knit in her spare time. She made the finest, delicate shawls, spencers (vests), stockings and socks. She made clothes for Gideon, but Lady Busta refused to put them on the boy, she wanted him dressed her way. When Barbara was allowed to take her son for a walk, she would take him up to her room and try some of the things on she had made for him, then hug him tight. He was her boy, after all, and he was lovely.

Lady Busta felt the need to take the boy completely under her wing. Sometimes he would come out with expressions his mother used, or talk about her in such a way as to make her Ladyship quite jealous. One day after a particularly heated argument with Barbara she said, "I've had enough from you girl, pack your things and get out of the house. I will not give you another chance."

"But Ma'am, I need to be here for Gideon, I am his mother," Barbara protested.

"Mother or not, you are going. He can only have one woman care for him, and I am that woman," said Lady Busta decidedly.

"But he needs me Ma'am, he is only a little boy, he will miss me," Barbara pleaded.

"Not if I have anything to do with it," shouted Elizabeth. "I brought up fourteen children, I can surely manage this one. Now go to your room and pack your things."

Barbara went to the kitchen and told Martha, who was very upset. "I will do what I can to help," she assured the distraught girl. "But what about yourself? You are not well, and where will you live?"

"I shall go to my mother's house in Lerwick, I suppose," answered Barbara, "but how can I leave my boy? It will break my heart, and he needs me at his age."

Thomas Gifford, coming in the front door at that moment, met Barbara going up the stairs.

"Whatever is the matter?" he asked as he looked at the distraught girl.

"Lady Busta has told me I have to leave here, and I can't take my little boy with me. What am I to do? He is my child and I love him and he needs me," she ended running up the stairs.

Thomas went to the sitting-room to find his wife sitting with her latest embroidery.

"What have you been saying to Barbara that she is so upset? I saw her just now in tears," asked Thomas.

"I have told her to leave, she has too much influence on the boy. He comes out with expressions she uses and talks too much about her," accused Elizabeth, hoping she had made her point.

"But of course he is going to talk of his mother. She is kind to him and you can see the look of love which passes between them. They are devoted to one another," said Thomas innocently.

"That is the very reason why I am separating them," hissed Elizabeth, "I hate her and will not have her in the house."

"Betty, how can you do this to the girl?" he asked.

"Enough is enough," shrieked Elizabeth.

Thomas left her to her sewing.

......

Barbara had long ago been banished to the kitchen at meal times, but Gideon sat with his grandparents, for etiquette's sake.

During the week Lady Busta told Gideon that his mother was going to Lerwick for a few days holiday but would be back before long. However, Barbara had always been honest with her son and now told him she was going away to stay at her mother's home in Lerwick as Lady Busta no longer needed her help. Beth was coming back to stay for good.

"Oh, great," shouted Gideon when he heard about Beth, but he clung to his mother and cried when he thought of her not being in the house with him.

"When you come to Lerwick, you can come and visit me," she said hopefully, "and I will always hear how you are getting on when anyone from Busta comes to town. You are to be a good boy and do as Lady Busta tells you, she has no patience with people who annoy her. I would love to leave something of mine with you, but it would be no use, she would just take it away. So, my darling, all I can give you is my dearest love and you will always be near my heart."

"Mother, do not cry for me," said Gideon bravely, "I shall be good and when I grow older, I will come and see you."

"Thank you, my love," whispered Barbara, hugging her son to her.

On the day of Barbara's departure, Lady Busta sent Martha to bring Gideon to the sitting-room.

The moment had come for Barbara to leave and she did not want Gideon to see his mother, in case there was a scene.

Gideon followed Martha to the sitting-room and sat on a stool at her Ladyship's feet.

"I want you to read to me," she began, "one of the favourite stories your tutor has taught you lately".

Selecting a book from the bookcase, Gideon proceeded to read a passage. Hearing a gig on the road, Gideon jumped up and looked out of the window.

"It's Grandfather," he shouted.

"Sit down at once," commanded Lady Busta, seeing all her carefully laid plans going astray. "I did not tell you to stop reading." Her words fell on deaf ears, for, out of the window Gideon saw his mother carrying her cloth bag and Martha and Beth following, with his mother's basket she had packed.

"Mother, Mother," he shouted and ran to the door.

"Come here at once," exploded Elizabeth, but to no avail. Gideon was down those stairs like a streak of lightning and out of the front door,

"Mother," he called, "wait for me."

Barbara stopped half-way down the Willow Walk – she was determined to leave Busta House in style, by the front door. She turned to see Gideon coming after her. He had outwitted Lady Busta this time.

Mother and son clung to each other for one precious moment.

"You can't go without me," cried Gideon.

"My dear, I am afraid I have to," answered Barbara. "Look, there is your Grandfather."

Thomas alighted from the gig and came slowly down the steps.

"You are leaving then Barbara?" he said in a strained voice. "Come, Gideon, I will take care of you, your Mother need have no fear."

Taking Gideon by the hand, Thomas Gifford led the little boy in a kindly way, back to the house, talking to him all the time.

Barbara did not look back, but she knew her son was in good hands with the Laird.

Peter saw that Barbara was settled in the boat, then rowed for Olnafirth. The young mother tried to be brave, but eventually broke down and sobbed and sobbed. She kept repeating her son's name over and over again.

Peter tried to comfort her by saying soothing things, that it would not be long till she saw her son again, but Barbara's spirit which had kept her brave for so long, seemed to have crumbled.

Arriving at Olnafirth, Peter carried Barbara's luggage to the waiting ponies which would take passengers to a boat at Catfirth bound for Lerwick.

"If I hear of anyone going to Lerwick," he told Barbara, "I will send them along to see you and they will tell you how Master Gideon is getting on. He will be all right with Thomas Gifford."

Barbara nodded her head.

"Thanks," she whispered.

......

Lady Busta heaved a sigh of relief as she heard the front door close. She had watched the whole proceedings from her sitting-room window. Barbara leaving the house by the Willow Walk and Martha and Beth helping to carry her worldly belongings. A tear escaped her eye as she saw Barbara Pitcairn walk proudly down the steps clutching her cloth bag, leaving with less in it than when she arrived. Had she been too hard on the girl? It was too late to call her back now. She saw Thomas walk towards the little group and watch, as mother and son embraced. He gently detached the boy from his mother and, hand in hand retraced their steps up to the front door.

A lump came into Elizabeth's throat, it was too much for her. She left the room and went to her bedroom, where she broke down and cried. Drying her eyes, she went to the chest-of-drawers for a clean handkerchief – and there was the drawer which held the secret compartment holding the marriage certificate! It was surely not too late to remove it and let Thomas see it. Barbara was as attached to Gideon as she had been to John but then she would look foolish if she produced it now. No. It was better to let sleeping dogs lie and she left the room.

At dinner that evening, Elizabeth tried to cheer Gideon up by saying, "Your tutor Rev William Jack will be with you tomorrow, he is very pleased with your progress. He will be staying at the house.".

"Thank you", said the boy. He would say no more the rest of the meal.

Gideon was very brave and it was only at night-time when he had gone to bed that he broke down and sobbed his little heart out, saying, "Why Mother did you have to leave me? I love you so much, I hope it won't be long till you come back again. I will always love you. Please God, look after Mother and keep her well."

Getting into bed Gideon snuggled down under the warm Shetland blankets and dreamt of happier days with his mother.

......

Thomas Gifford thought long and hard about Gideon. He was a lovely boy and a promising student. He was like John in so many ways and he decided once and for all that Gideon would be the beneficiary in his estate.

If Gideon had not been born, then Andrina's son Andrew would have been heir to the estate, however Thomas had accepted Gideon as John's son.

Thomas executed a deed of entail, leaving the estate to, 'my grandson, procreate of the body of John Gifford, my eldest lawful son'. Four years later, a bond was made out over the estate of Busta for £10,000 in favour of Gideon Gifford, in case any legal difficulties might arise to prevent him taking possession.

Next morning Thomas Gifford took Gideon into his study and talked to him about his role as son of the house. Although he was young, yet he would take the place of the son Thomas had lost.

It was difficult for Gideon to keep his mind on lessons that day, when Rev Jack arrived.

"Is something wrong Gideon, you are not concentrating today?" asked his tutor.

"No, sir, I shall be fine," said Gideon bravely, then tears began to run down his sad face.

"Come on, tell me what it is that is worrying you," Rev Jack said kindly.

"My mother, she left yesterday," he sobbed.

"But she will be back soon," the tutor assured the boy.

"I am afraid not sir, she has gone for good. I am to be brought up by my grandparents," he managed to say.

The boy was so upset and trying to be brave. Rev Jack got up, and putting an arm round his shoulder said, "I think we will leave lessons today shall we? I feel more like going for a ride. Would your grieve fix me up with a pony and we will get Martha to make a picnic for us. What do you say, lad?"

"That would be great," said a decidedly more cheerful voice.

"Right, shut books for today and we will go to the stables," said William Jack.

The ride to the other side of the island was pleasant, and they stopped beside a cove. The picnic was a great success and as the couple neared Busta House again, the tutor stopped his pony and came and stood beside Gideon and said, "Your grandparents love you and want the best for you. It is difficult for two women to bring up a boy and Lady Busta feels she has everything to offer you, education, secure future and a beautiful home."

"My Mother had very little, I know", admitted Gideon, "but at least she loved me."

Looking down on Busta House, Gideon made up his mind, for his dear Mother's sake, that he would be the son she wanted him to be, brave, honest, courteous and kind.

Mounting their ponies again, the pair wended their way down the hill to the stable. Gideon told his tutor he would rub the ponies down then join the party at dinner later.

That evening Thomas and Elizabeth were quite surprised at Gideon's change of attitude. He spoke when spoken to and seemed to enjoy his meal.

In the drawing-room afterwards he played a game of chess with Rev Jack and won.

"I shall be up to turn out your lamp," said Elizabeth as Gideon bade them all goodnight.

"That is very thoughtful of you Grandmother," said the boy, "but I shall manage it quite well. Thank you, goodnight."

Passing by his bedroom door, Gideon made his way up the small attic stairs to where his mother's bedroom was. He knew where she kept the candle and, lighting it from a lamp on the stairway, went into the bedroom.

What he hoped to find, he did not know. A new servant was coming tomorrow and he felt he had to have a look round to see if his mother had left anything.

Holding the candle in one hand, he silently opened the drawers of the small chest, nothing there. A cupboard in the corner was empty also. The bed had been made up with clean blankets for the next occupant.

Just as Gideon was about to blow out the candle, he saw something glitter behind the door. It was the brooch his mother always wore to keep her shawl together. Picking it up gently, he put it in his pocket. He had something of hers after all. He went to bed happy.

......

Meanwhile, Barbara arrived in Lerwick after a long, cold journey on the boat. She did not, however, feel the cold as her mind and thoughts were of her son at Busta House. Alighting at the small pier, she carried her possessions the short walk to her mother's house. It was facing the sea and overlooked the main thoroughfare, 97 Commercial Street. The small house was approached by a narrow lane. The windows looked down onto the street below where people walked all day going about their business. Foreigners also tramped the stone-paved street and the Dutchmen's clogs made a noise on the stone flags. The Dutch called Lerwick 'Bus-haven' as they made that their place of rendezvous before starting out to the herring fishing.

How different it all was to Busta House with its wide carpeted staircase, large rooms, huge garden and rolling hills beyond. Freedom, but alas no joy.

Barbara unpacked the few articles she had taken with her. Her thoughts were constantly with Gideon. How was she to survive without him? She had no money unless she knitted each day and sold her garments to the shops. Being an expert knitter of the finest Shetland wool, she was able to sell all that she made.

Many a day Barbara would watch from her window as the Gifford family, in town for the day, paraded the street, looking in the windows of the few shops, then going to the hotel for a meal, but Gideon was never with them.

...

Gideon often wondered who his father was. He was told he had been drowned before Gideon was born. No one would tell him any more. Maybe grandfather would inform him some day. He often caught him looking at him in a strange way. One day he called him John.

Each day was filled to capacity, meals, lessons, riding, sailing and best of all, going with Grandfather in the gig to Brae.

Gideon longed for his mother – the gentle, kind, pretty woman who had been so good to him. As year after year went by he wondered why his mother had never returned, or why she had not written to him. Unknown to him and Barbara, Lady Busta had seen to it that no letters were ever delivered to Gideon and none sent out.

Chapter 24

GIDEON's PRESENT

There was great excitement in the kitchen at Busta House. Martha was going to Lerwick. Once a year she took a holiday and went to visit her sister. This time she was also looking forward to seeing Barbara Pitcairn. They all missed her so much and were heart-felt sorry for the boy who put on a brave face. Once or twice when Martha went into his room to make sure everything was in order, she would find little pictures drawn of a lady, she was sure it was Barbara.

The day before she left, she knocked on his door, "Gideon," she said – it only had to be "sir" when the grandparents were around, "I am hoping to go to Lerwick for two days tomorrow, and I shall visit your mother. Have you any message for her?"

"Oh, yes, Martha, I was up in her room the day she left here to check that she had not forgotten anything and I found her shawl brooch. Will you take it to her please? She told me she would not leave anything for me in case Lady Busta found it and took it away and, and," he stopped short, "sorry Martha I got carried away there. I am sorry. Yes, I will give you this for her." He added bravely, "I will also put in this drawing I did for her." He bowed his head as he sat down and tried not to cry. Martha, as always, was hurt for the boy. She went over to the bed and, putting an arm round him said,

"You poor boy, you have done so well. We all know how much you meant to each other. You are being very brave. If you want anything, any time, you just have to come to Martha and I will help you. I brought you into the world and I know how much it cost your dear mother, but no one will ever know how much it cost her to have to leave you here." Martha was near to tears herself.

"Thank you Martha," said Gideon patting her hand, "I will tell you if I need your help."

"Now Master Gideon, have that message ready for me at dinner time. When I come to light your lamp, I shall look under your pillow," said practical Martha as she shut the door.

Gideon found a piece of paper in which a book had been sent to him, and wrapping the brooch in a handkerchief, placed it and the little picture in the parcel. Putting it in his pocket, he went down to dinner.

When his grandparents entered the drawing-room after the meal, Gideon excused himself for a moment. He made his way to Grandfather's study and did exactly as he had seen him do many times to letters. He lit a taper and held it to a piece of seal-wax over the parcel, thus sealing the opening. Rushing up stairs he popped the parcel under his pillow.

Martha lit the lamps in the bedrooms. Putting her hand under Gideon's pillow she found the parcel tied with a piece of wool, but also sealed with wax.

"Dear brave boy," she said to herself.

The next day dawned fair and Martha, with her large, covered basket left the house to walk to the pier. Gideon saw her and ran after her saying he would carry the basket to the boat.

"Have you got my parcel?" he asked eagerly.

"I have that!" replied Martha, patting her pocket.

"Thank you Martha, you are a friend," he said handing her the basket. Turning, he ran back to the house, happier than he had been for a long time.

......

Patrick and Andrina of Ollabery had a happy home. They had two sons, Andrew and Thomas and one daughter, Elizabeth.

Unfortunately, seven years after their marriage, Andrina became ill and died. Patrick also became ill and died that same year.

Lady Busta was very upset. She received the three children into her home.

Gideon was eleven years of age and now had to contend with three younger children in the house. It could not have been easy for him, after having the run of the place to himself, to share everything, even his grandparents.

It was a generous gesture on the part of Elizabeth, as she was now a woman of some years, but these were Andrina's children, her own grandchildren, and she, had to look after them.

These three children stayed at Busta House for some years until a suitable housekeeper was found and they returned to Ollaberry.

Chapter 25

DEATH OF THOMAS GIFFORD

Gideon usually walked with his grandfather each morning to the Booth and accompanied him round the store. He listened carefully as Thomas spoke to the men about their work and the necessary provisions to be ordered.

Angus brought Jasper and the gig to the door to await his master's going to Brae.

One morning Gideon said he would like to take Gypsy to Brae as he enjoyed the ride. Excusing himself from the breakfast-table he went to the stable to inform Angus that he was taking the pony.

Left on their own, Lady Busta was surprised to see her husband looking somewhat pale.

"Thomas, are you feeling all right?" she asked anxiously.

"I do feel a bit tired," he admitted, "it has been a particularly busy time lately and with the last order of salt not being delivered it has thrown everything into chaos. The fish cannot be salted or sold – the men have to do without their wages. I shall go to Brae anyhow and see what can be done".

Walking down the hill to the Booth, Thomas felt a little dizzy but kept going. Angus met him after his consultation with the men there, then drove onto Brae, where another delegation of men awaited the Laird. After speaking to each in turn he felt exhausted. Gideon approached him and asked if it was time to go home for lunch yet.

"You are right, young man", said Thomas relieved to think that his morning was completed. Arriving at the Booth, Thomas alighted and went in to give a message to the foreman. Stepping outside again he stumbled and fell. Several men around came to his help. Angus told Gideon to ride to the house and tell Martha to get a bed ready for Master Thomas as he had collapsed. Gideon mounted Gypsy and in no time was at the front door. Meeting Martha he told her what had happened. Practical Martha soon had everything ready for the invalid, while Gideon ran upstairs to the sitting-room where he found Lady Busta.

"Grandmother," he started, "I was with Grandfather at the Booth just now and he fell as he was going to get into the gig." Gideon wiped a tear from his eye. He was being very brave and would not cry in front of a lady.

"Was he hurt?" Lady Busta asked.

"I do not know," replied the boy, "I just saw him lying on the ground. I was told to go straight away and tell Martha to get a bed ready for him. One of the men standing there was told to go to Sullom and fetch the doctor as he is usually there today."

A makeshift stretcher was made and the men carried Thomas up to the house. He had not regained consciousness and Lady Busta was beside herself with worry.

"I do trust the doctor gets here soon," she sobbed, as she saw her husband lying on the stretcher looking so ill.

The men carried their master into the library at Martha's request. After a few minutes Thomas opened his eyes and asked where he was.

"Don't you remember Grandfather?" asked Gideon anxiously, "you fell outside the Booth. Were you hurt when you fell? You will be all right, the doctor will be here soon."

Slowly sitting up, Thomas drank some water Martha had brought. The doctor arrived shortly afterwards. He was quite worried about the Laird's condition.

"Get him to bed at once," he ordered, "there are no broken bones. I think …", but he never got the words out as he heard a groan behind him and, looking round, saw the Laird's face distort for a second in pain, his eyes close and he fell back on the pillows.

Thomas Gifford of Busta had died.

"Can't you do something?" asked Lady Busta in agitation.

"I am sorry," replied the doctor, "but your husband has passed away."

Lady Busta sat down on a chair while Martha fetched the smelling salts. Gideon came and put an arm around her shoulders and Elizabeth patted his hand saying, "You are now the 'Laird of Busta' just as your Grandfather wished."

"Martha, take me to my room. See that Doctor Edwardson has a cup of tea before he leaves."

"Thank you Doctor for coming so promptly".

"Thank you Ma'am," he replied, "I shall leave something for you in case of delayed shock. This has all been so sudden."

On the day of the funeral it dawned a beautiful, sunny, morning with a calm sea. It was a sad little procession which Elizabeth watched from her sitting-room window as it wound its way from the front door down the driveway to the pier. Gideon walked in front of the chief mourners who were carrying the ornate coffin which was placed in a waiting boat draped in black. Many other boats left Brae to accompany the boat on its way to the voehead.

Arriving at the little pier, the men carried the coffin up to the church, where a service was conducted. The minister also officiated at the graveside.

The mourners returned to Busta House where Martha had a lovely meal ready for them. Lady Busta conducted herself in a gracious manner and accepted the condolences of all present.

It all seemed so strange to Gideon. At the age of twelve years he had a heavy burden on his young shoulders but Lady Busta made sure that everything would be done to keep the affairs of the estate in perfect running order until such time as he could take over the responsibility himself.

......

Three years after the death of Thomas Gifford in 1760, it was time for Gideon to attend college in Aberdeen. The time came for the young man to leave home, and although he was excited to be able to further his education, and looked forward to meeting other young people of his age outwith the island, he knew it was going to be very difficult to settle down to studies all day and each evening, after the freedom of Busta. He would miss his grandmother and friends, and all the animals he loved and tended so lovingly, especially Gypsy.

Lady Busta came to the front door to say goodbye to Gideon. She felt his leaving home greatly. He was all she had now. She waved as the gig went down the drive with Gideon, Angus, Rev Jack and all the luggage, making for the boat to take them to Olnafirth and thence to Lerwick.

Strict instructions had been given to the Rev Jack that when the ferry came alongside the south-bound ship, anchored in Bressay sound, he and the boy had to board it and on no condition were they to go into Lerwick. Lady Busta was still frightened that Barbara Pitcairn would kidnap her son.

Gideon settled well at King's College. His master, John Leslie wrote well of Gideon saying he was very sensible and possessed of much sweetness of disposition and that Rev Jack devoted his whole time to being useful to him. He could not have been fonder of him had he been his own son.

Each year as Gideon left home the same instructions were given to the Rev Jack,

"Get on the boat immediately and do not enter Lerwick."

However, when Gideon was 17 years of age, this pattern changed. On entering Lerwick harbour in the ferry, they found that the mail-boat was overdue and the ferry had to land at Lerwick jetty to await its arrival.

Gideon calmly asked Rev Jack if he could show him where his mother lived, adding, "I would dearly love to see her again."

"I have kept my side of the bargain to your Grandmother not to enter Lerwick," Rev Jack replied, "but this time the situation is out of my hands. You are old enough now to make up your own mind whether to see her or not. The house is along the shore here and up that lane," the tutor said, pointing in the direction of Norna's Court.

"Thank you," said Gideon and he left the tutor saying he would join him again when he sighted the boat, from the window, entering the harbour.

Chapter 26

GIDEON VISITS HIS MOTHER

Gideon knocked on the door.

Unprepared for a visitor, Barbara laid aside her knitting, straightened her pretty blue camelot gown, which was still one of her nice dresses from Busta days, and opened the door.

On seeing a young man standing there, she nearly asked his name. Then she recognised the boy, her own son, John! He was the image of his father. Handsomely dressed, tall and distinguished looking.

"Gideon," she corrected herself in time.

"Mother," he said, taking her hand, "did you not recognise me?"

"Yes," she said, "come in. I knew it was you, how could I forget? Will you sit down? I shall make some tea."

Busying herself, Barbara was able to think more clearly. It was actually Gideon who was here, she could hardly believe it.

Putting a few peats on the open fire, she filled the kettle with a cup from a small bucket of water which stood on a shelf. She hung the kettle on the hook which hung down from the chimney. Taking some biscuits from a small tin, she put them on a plate. From a drawer she took out a lace cloth which she put on the table. When tea was ready they sat and talked. It seemed so strange, this young man, was her son, yet they felt like strangers.

"Do tell me Gideon how you are getting along at Busta? Is her Ladyship well?" asked Barbara bravely.

"Thank you Mother, she is fine, still ordering me about!" Gideon laughed. The ice was broken!

"How are Martha and Beth?" queried Barbara, "are they still at Busta?"

"Martha is still there, but Beth left when her family came along, so her sister is there instead. Peter the boatman died. I liked Peter. He told me how upset you were when you left Busta House that day. Mother, it is ten years ago.

Grandfather told me all about you and that is why I am here today. I just wanted to see you for myself, that you are all right." So saying he rose from his chair and put his arm round his mother's shoulders.

"I will never forget you, Mother," he said kneeling beside her, "I have always loved you. You were so gentle and kind to me. At first I could not understand why you did not come back, but now I do. I can't bear to think of all you went through for me. You must have felt so terrible when Father was drowned. Grandfather told me the story. If they had had proof of the marriage, it would have helped."

"But there was proof, Gideon. I took the certificate from your father's pocket when he lay dead on the beach," she replied.

"Well, what happened to it?" Gideon asked puzzled.

"I put it in my pocket," said Barbara, "but someone must have come into my room when I was asleep and taken it. But I have my own proof here."

Barbara took a ring from round her neck. "This is the ring your Father gave me when we were married. I have worn it every day since. I was told not to wear it on my hand in case the Giffords saw it, so I keep it here. I will give it to you now. It is inscribed with our initials inside. Never let Lady Busta see it."

Gideon smiled, "You still have a good spirit in you!" Placing the ring on his finger he added, "I shall wear this ring for all to see."

"I had better be going now, Mother. I have enjoyed our time together. I will always treasure your gift to me."

Gideon bent and kissed his Mother.

"God bless you," was all Barbara could say as she waved goodbye to her son. Little did she know that this was the last time she would see him, but how wonderful his visit had been. It reawakened some of the happiest memories of their times together.

Chapter 27

DEATH OF LADY BUSTA

Relaxing in the sitting-room one afternoon, Elizabeth was handed the latest letter from the Rev William Jack. How she loved to read of Gideon and the different subjects he was taking. If only Thomas had lived to read them too and see his faith in the boy being rewarded.

On an impulse, Elizabeth thought of Barbara. She too would have been so proud of her son. She would write a note and tell her. Rising, she went to the writing bureau and took a sheet of headed notepaper. Lifting the quill to dip it in the ink, she changed her mind. She had vowed never to forgive the girl, so why bother now? Putting the paper carefully back on the pad she closed the bureau and sat down.

Lifting the latest embroidery from her workbox, she ran her fingers over the polished wood remembering the day Thomas had proudly presented it to her. What a lot had happened since that day. Five dear children lost at once with the smallpox, then four boys drowned together. Fortunately there were other children, but only one daughter now remained, Christina, Lady Symbister.

Lady Busta, 'that proud Lady' wept. Ringing the bell, she asked Martha to bring a cup of her favourite tea. That would cheer her up.

......

Gideon had heard rumours to the effect that he was illegitimate, how degrading, yet Grandfather always spoke to him as if he was his own grandson. When Gideon enquired about his own father, Grandfather had always made excuses to talk of something else. It was exceedingly frustrating. When people asked how his father was employed he answered he had been drowned. Grandfather had eventually told Gideon the truth.

After seeing his mother so badly treated, and not knowing his proper identity, Gideon became embittered and his temper broke.

Lady Busta herself was becoming weaker. After all she had been through her spirit seemed to have given way. Thomas had always been by her side. Still, it would not be long before Gideon finished his studies and came home to take up the work of the estate his grandfather had left him. He would then be the true 'Laird of Busta'.

When news of his home-coming reached her Ladyship, she determined to make the most of it. Cook laid on a wonderful meal. She and Gideon ate in style that evening – the lamps and candles lit, sent a warm glow round the room and reflected the light on the family silver and crystal.

"Grandmother," said Gideon, "it is good to be home again. I shall take up where Grandfather left off. You will need to take more care of yourself, you look a bit tired!"

"Oh, nonsense," objected her Ladyship sitting up straight in her chair, "I am fine. There is nothing coming over me."

Gideon was a very handsome young man now and Lady Busta was exceedingly proud of him. He tended to be more of the Highland Laird than the Shetland proprietor. Having mixed with the Scottish nobility at college he was more acquaint with their manner. He dined sumptuously and entertained extensively, both friends and strangers.

Lady Busta was growing weaker each day. Something was bothering her very much. All the years since putting Barbara Pitcairn out of the house, she had had a bad conscience. Bringing up Gideon had been a pleasure, but what of his mother? She must have loved John and he must have loved her to have had a secret marriage. What could she do?

Going to the bedroom she removed a bundle of letters she had tied up for her daughter Christina to receive when she died.

A thought struck her. Why not write a letter to her daughter, Lady Symbister, requesting her, after Lady Busta's death, to make public the marriage certificate and tell everyone they could that the marriage had been legal after all. It would salve her conscience at the moment and yet make sure that justice had been done.

Taking paper from her bureau she sat down and wrote to her daughter. Putting the letter into the bundle of letters, she thought she would have one last look at the marriage certificate.

On opening it, she began to read the contents. Just at that moment a knock came to the door. Quickly, Elizabeth put the certificate into the recently written letter in the bundle and closed the drawer.

"Come in," she shouted.

"Grandmother, whatever are you doing here?" asked Gideon.

"Dinner was served a while ago. I have been waiting for you."

"Sorry Gideon, I got rather carried away looking over some old letters," she replied a bit flustered.

"By the way," she added as Gideon guided her to the dining-room, "I should like Christina to have the chest-of-drawers in my bedroom after I am gone."

"Don't worry," Gideon assured her, "I shall certainly see to that, but let us have a happy meal tonight, just the two of us."

In the drawing-room after dinner, Lady Busta sat thinking of the certificate. Once she got up to her room to go to bed, she would remove it and put it in the inner secret drawer again.

As Gideon sat reading a paper, he heard a choking sound, and, looking up, saw his Grandmother going blue in the face. He rang the bell and immediately Martha came into the room.

"Send Angus for the doctor," he ordered her, "then come and help me to get her Ladyship to bed."

Lifting Lady Busta in his arms he carried her upstairs. She was a shadow of herself now, so different from the over-bearing person some years previously. When Doctor Edwardson arrived he pronounced her dead.

Gideon was very upset. Although Lady Busta had treated his own mother so badly, she had certainly given him all he had needed and she had loved him in her own peculiar way.

After the death of Lady Busta, Gideon and Lady Symbister, his aunt, talked of days gone by.

"I would like you to choose something of Grandmother's that you would really like," Gideon told her. "Furniture, jewellery or anything you might have admired or longed for."

"I would really love the old chest-of-drawers in her bedroom," Christina replied, "when we were children we would love to play hide and seek in the rooms and I always hid beside the old chest and traced the carvings with my fingers as I waited for the person to find me."

"Yes, it is a fine old piece of furniture. Actually that was the one article that Grandmother expressly wanted you to have. I shall get it sent to you as soon as I can. What about her workbox?" asked Gideon.

"I would really treasure that also," Aunt Christina said, dabbing her eyes with a little lace handkerchief, "Mother always loved to tell us the story of how father got it for her."

"You will have to come and visit me here again sometime," said Gideon. "I shall be quite lonely. To think that this house used to be full at one time. I shall try and keep it as grandfather would have liked it."

"I am sure you will," said Christina getting ready to leave in the gig.

About a month later a large container arrived at Symbister House. It proved to be the case in which the chest-of-drawers was packed. Lady Symbister had it put straight into the attic lumber room. It would have to be thoroughly cleaned before use and there was nowhere in the house at that moment to place it.

Gideon realised that while his grandmother was alive, no other woman would be welcomed at Busta House. He had often gone with his grandfather to Lochend to visit the Nicolson family there. One of the daughters, Grizel or Grace, was a beautiful girl and she and Gideon often talked together on these visits. She had a wonderful way of listening to other people and also had great patience in helping others. Gideon's love for her grew deeper each time he saw her and she likewise reciprocated his feelings.

After the death of Lady Busta, Gideon went to Lochend to visit Mr Arthur Nicolson with the sole intention of asking for the hand of his daughter in marriage. Both Mr and Mrs Nicolson were happy to give their consent, knowing that their daughter would have a happy life with Gideon Gifford of Busta.

Grizel proved to be a loving and affectionate partner to her husband who often confided in her on business matters. They had a large family of six children. Four daughters – Bess, Grace, Jessie and Christian. The boys were Arthur and Thomas. Other children were also born to them who did not survive.

Busta House was once more a happy home with the sound of children's laughter. But all too soon they grew up.

Chapter 28

THE MARRIAGE CERTIFICATE

Lady Symbister was making a dress and required a length of black lace. "I know there was a large piece somewhere," she told Jane the maid, "help me to look for it. I have searched all over the house. It might be in a box in the attic, come, we will look there."

"Shall I look in this old chest Ma'am?" enquired Jane.

"No, no," replied Lady Symbister "that was my mother's. But, wait a minute, while we are up here I might as well have a peep in the old thing. I just got it because it held so many childhood memories for me."

The drawers were all opened and the contents of each examined.

"This one is stuck," said her Ladyship, "it is a small one, and I cannot seem to move it. It seems locked."

"Can I try it, Ma'am?" Jane offered, "I see there is a small brass circle at the side. Shall I push it?".

"Certainly," cried Lady Symbister excitedly.

Jane pressed the brass circle and at once the front of the imitation drawer flew open! revealing a small parcel, wrapped in gray paper.

"Ma'am," said Jane, "what is this? Will I throw it out?"

"No, no," shrieked Lady Symbister, "it is maybe something of value. Give it to me."

"What is it?" she asked herself, "letters of some kind. Yes, here is one from Mother, that is why she wanted me to have this chest. You look for that lace will you while I read this note?"

"Yes Ma'am," Jane obediently replied. "Is this, the lace, in this old hat-box."

There was no reply, and Jane turned in time to see Lady Symbister going white and falling to the floor. Jane flew downstairs and returned with water, her mistress could not speak.

Poor Jane could get no sense from Lady Symbister, who just pointed to the certificate on the floor. Jane picked it up, read it and looked shocked.

"But listen to this," whispered her Ladyship, when she had found her voice again. "There is a letter in with it. My Mother has left me her dying blessing. She says she will carry her resentment of Barbara Pitcairn to her dying day, but once she has gone, I am to tell the news to everyone, that her son John really was married to Barbara Pitcairn, and if need be, show the certificate to anyone who does not believe me."

Jane sank down on to the floor saying, "Ma'am, fancy finding that after all these years. But who would have hidden them in there?" she asked in all innocence.

"My Mother!" replied her Ladyship with vehemence, "My Mother! To think of the awful life she put Barbara through, and in the end banished her from Busta House. I cannot think how she could have done this to poor Barbara. We all loved her. Mother knew about the marriage all the time and never told anyone."

Folding up the certificate and letters her Ladyship once more placed the fated parcel in the secret drawer. Jane was sworn to secrecy.

Her Ladyship's first instinct was to write and tell Gideon of the find, but as each day passed she felt more ashamed of the way her mother had treated Gideon's mother and could not bring herself to mention it, and so, the certificate was locked away in the old chest for a few more years when it was brought to light again with devastating results.

Lady Symbister did not keep well and shortly after an illness she died. A sale was held at the house in 1802 and several people gathered for the auction, among them Andrew Gifford of Ollaberry, cousin of Gideon, thinking he might pick up a bargain.

Seeing the chest going under the hammer, he bid for it. It was a trifle too large for most houses so he obtained it easily. Pleased with himself, Andrew had the chest shipped over once more to the mainland, and his estate in Ollaberry. He was very fond of the old piece of family furniture and kept it in his study. Each day he went through a different drawer looking at the old papers and documents his grandmother had stored there. Coming to the top drawer, he opened it and found the secret drawer behind. He noticed the little metal circle, which he pressed and suddenly the drawer opened. Taking out an old paper parcel he was intrigued as to why anyone would want to keep such an old, dirty wrapper. Unfolding it eagerly, he was paralysed with fear as he read the contents.

John and Barbara's marriage certificate. So it was true after all. 'But,' he reminisced, 'this is in the chest which used to be in Grandmother's bedroom. How did it get there? I wonder if Christina knew it was there? If she did, why did she not tell everyone. This letter from grandmother says she has to let everyone know the truth. Maybe she never found the certificate.'

An idea began to form in Andrew's head, a pecuniary one of course. He would write Gideon and tell him that he had bought the old chest that had belonged to his grandmother, and, while clearing out a drawer had come across John and Barbara Pitcairns' wedding certificate. This proved beyond all doubt that he was the legitimate grandson of Thomas and Elizabeth Gifford.

Andrew owed Gideon a considerable amount of money and now he suggested that in order to obtain the certificate, he, Gideon, would have to cancel all debts owing to him and the document would be his.

Andrew enjoyed writing the letter, so sure was he that his cousin would want his name cleared of all suspicious circumstances and act immediately.

But it was not to be so.

When Gideon received the letter from his cousin in Ollaberry he thought it was a plea for more money to help Andrew out of some difficulty. In a way he was quite correct.

After reading Andrew of Ollaberry's proposal for Gideon to cancel all his debts on being handed the marriage certificate, Gideon and his son Arthur, spent many hours discussing the prospect of whether to accept the certificate and once and for all end the stories which had been handed down over the years making Gideon the illegitimate grandson of the Laird of Busta.

Finally, Gideon decided that had the certificate been discovered while his mother was living it would have been advantageous for her sake to clear her name. But she, to whom it was most important, was not living.

Thomas Gifford, also deceased, would have appreciated the fact that he had made the right decision in appointing Gideon as his heir.

......

Grizel's sister, Andrina Nicolson of Lochend, was married to Andrew of Ollaberry, but her life, unlike that of her sister's was a sad one. The Rev P. Barclay said of Andrew, 'he was an industrious man but did not manage his own affairs well. His moral qualities were not admirable'.

Andrew and Andrina had a family of ten children. Gideon was kind to them and often helped them out in difficult times. Two of the five daughters died, but the three remaining ones married well. Of the five sons, four died and Arthur remained.

The Ollaberry family always believed that Gideon was illegitimate and that the Busta Estate should really belong to them. They felt that their Grandfather had exceeded his powers in leaving it to Gideon.

Gideon's son Arthur was very like his great grandmother, Elizabeth Gifford, haughty and domineering.

When Andrew of Ollaberry's letter arrived with a copy of the marriage certificate, Gideon and Arthur refused to be bribed by Andrew into paying off his debts for the return of the certificate.

Later, however, they agreed to Andrew's terms, but by this time he said he had lost the certificate.

Gideon and Arthur were furious.

Meantime, Andrew wrote to Mr David Balfour, Gideon's lawyer in Edinburgh, and explained the situation. He enclosed the certificate which had come to light after fifty-eight years. It read: At Busta, 8th December, 1747. These certify that this day, John Gifford of Busta, younger, and Barbara Pitcairn, there were duly married in the presence of William Gifford and Hay Gifford, his brothers, by

John Fiskin, Minister.

William Gifford, Witness.

Hay Gifford, Witness.

......

Gideon's health was now failing and his son Arthur acted as amanuensis for his father. Between 1808 and 1810 many letters passed between the young Laird of Busta and Andrew of Ollaberry. Ollaberry threatening, while Busta still held him to ransom for £300.

Once or twice an agreement would be made only to be broken. In right, Andrew should have handed over the certificate to Gideon who would have given him a handsome reward for it. He might also have cancelled much of Andrew's debt as he was giving up his chance of succeeding to the Busta Estate for ever.

Andrew of Ollaberry died in 1810. His wife survived him until 1830. Their son Arthur took up the case against his cousin.

Although Arthur Gifford of Busta was a haughty young man, he must have acquired something of the hospitable nature of his father and great grandmother, because he paid his Aunt Andrina an annuity, despite her pride and hurt feelings.

......

Gideon and Grizel lived happily together until May 1811.

At dinner one evening Gideon complained of a sore head. Grizel took him through to the drawing-room where he collapsed and died.

Poor Grizel was desperately upset and all Arthur did to comfort her seemed in vain.

Next evening as the family were gathered in the drawing-room and Arthur was explaining something to his sisters, he turned to ask his mother's advice but she did not reply. Looking up, Arthur saw that she also had passed away.

It was sad, but, as the couple had been so devoted to one another it seemed that one could not exist without the other.

They were buried together.

'As they were pleasant and devoted to each other in their lives, so in death they were not divided.'

......

After Andrina's death, Arthur, looking through some of his mother's papers was finally roused to take action against Arthur of Busta. One lawsuit led to another.

On 3rd February, 1856 Arthur Gifford, of Busta died, aged 69, without issue. The estate was heavily in debt to the sum of £32,000, partly as a result of the first law-suit in the Court of Session.

Lawyers and Trustees took over the estate, while Factors, who lived in the house, managed the estate.

Arthur Gifford of Busta left instructions to pay off the debts of the estate then hand the estate over to the nearest male heir alive at that time. None was found.

By January 1921 the last of the annuitants died unmarried. Since then the Manor House has passed into private ownership and is now a top-class country hotel.

The 'House of Busta' is long gone, but Busta House still stands proudly at the head of Busta Voe.

It is said that Barbara Pitcairn still roams the house looking for her son John.